BRIGHTER PLANETS

EARL C. SLIPHER

This work includes some of the best photographic sequences obtained during a lifetime study of the planets by one man, Earl C. Slipher (1883-). His first plate was made with the Lowell 24-inch telescope in January, 1907 and the last was made with the same instrument 56 years later. This frontispiece was selected for this book by the editor as a well-deserved tribute to its author.

A Photographic Study
of the
BRIGHTER
PLANETS

by EARL C. SLIPHER, Sc.D., LL.D.
Astronomer, Lowell Observatory

Published in 1964 by
Lowell Observatory, Flagstaff, Arizona
and the
National Geographic Society, Washington, D.C.

EDITOR

JOHN S. HALL

Director
Lowell Observatory

COPYRIGHT 1964

NATIONAL GEOGRAPHIC SOCIETY and

LOWELL OBSERVATORY

Library of Congress Catalog No. 64-18807

PRINTED IN THE UNITED STATES OF AMERICA

BY NORTHLAND PRESS, FLAGSTAFF, ARIZONA

FOREWORD

Early in this century, in the year 1905, I began a lifetime of work devoted to observing, studying, and most important, photographing the planets. This publication represents an attempt to present in the most adequate manner some of the highlights that have resulted from this effort.

This volume must be essentially pictorial in nature. However, many of the original negatives in the vaults of the Lowell Observatory have star trails impressed upon them to mark their orientation in the telescope, and (since 1922) contain standarized light scales. Consequently, the plate collection may be quantitatively used for both positional and photometric purposes.

Because planetary photography at the Lowell Observatory was intended from the start as an incontestable record for studying changes on the planets, the prevailing idea was to secure a series of photographs as homogeneous as possible for critical analysis and inter-comparison. Naturally, those planets which exhibited the most rapid changes have received the most attention while the earth-like character of Mars has led to special emphasis on its study.

This unique collection of photographs, taken during an interval of nearly sixty years, should record the entire gamut of change that any planet may undergo in a very long time. Some of the photographs deal with the nature of the surface of the planet Mercury. Others record the behavior of the perpetually cloud-covered Venus and changes in the ultraviolet photographs. Still others record the ever-changing cloud belts on giant Jupiter and the cloud belts on beautiful Saturn. Many of the photographs record interesting changes on Mars: seasonal changes in the snow caps and the darkening of the dark regions; Martian clouds and atmospheric phenomena; secular changes and temporary dark areas; and the problem of the Martian blue haze and blue clearing.

This book is being published in two editions: a limited edition in which only actual photographic reproductions are used, and a more general edition containing the usual half-tone reproductions. The limited edition is expected to preserve nearly all of the details on the original negatives and is to be made available to those actively engaged in planetary work.

Most of the photographs reproduced here were obtained at Flagstaff with the Lowell 24-inch refractor. A few were made with the Lowell 42-inch reflector and many Martian plates were made with the Lamont-Hussey 27½-inch refractor in South Africa. In addition, in 1907 an expedition was made to Tarapaca, Chile, South America, using the Amherst 18-inch refractor. The three refractors yielded excellent planetary images, but correcting lenses were used with the 24-inch and 27½-inch for the far infrared, and for the blue and violet, in order that the light could be focused for different ranges throughout the entire photographic spectrum.

Highest quality photographs of the planets are essential to the proper interpretation of planetary characteristics. The eye can record the occasional moments of superb seeing, but photographs can rarely catch such brief intervals. Photographs, however, are objective, and though exposure conditions may be very different, photographs from various observatories and observers can be made comparable when the knowledge of emulsions, filters, and development is taken into consideration.

For a planet, like Jupiter, where the complexity of detail is so great that it is impossible to make detailed drawings in the interval limited by the planet's rotation, the photograph completely records everything in situ in less than one second. Color filters may be used to record quantitatively the colors of the bands of Jupiter and Saturn, and their changes.

Only through photographs can we objectively record the seasonal or secular changes of planetary features. Photographs therefore, present the most effective way to measure the motion of, and the changes in planetary detail.

Planetary photography is an art which requires meticulous care, persistence, and the use of many personal skills and techniques. One must learn to take advantage of those moments when the seeing is best, to recognize and check unusual phenomena, and maintain a vigilance over them, even when conditions are unfavorable. At Flagstaff a 12-inch refractor, attached to the 24-inch, was used to monitor the seeing. With a power of about 1500 I made exposures only at moments of best seeing and found that this procedure greatly increased the percentage of good images.

Publication of this book has been made possible through the generous help of the National Geographic Society. In addition, two of the expeditions to South Africa, where many of the Martian photographs were taken, were financed in large measure by National Geographic funds, and the Society has rendered valuable assistance in the final reproduction and enlargement of many plates in this volume. It is my hope that it will provide an appropriate planetary curtain for the stellar background so magnificiently portrayed by the National Geographic Society—Palomar Observatory Sky Survey.

In 1962 with the assistance of the Aeronautical Chart and Information Center of the United States Air Force a large number of Martian photographs were published;[1] a portion of these are reproduced in this volume. More than half of the plates presented here, however, show the most informative and illustrative pictures of the other bright planets in the solar system.

In the author's earlier book on Mars, acknowledgments were made to the many observatories, universities, governments, and especially to the host of devoted individuals who helped in its prepara-

---

[1]Slipher, E. C., 1962, *The Photographic Story of Mars*, Sky Publishing Corp., Cambridge, Mass. and Northland Press, Flagstaff, Ariz.

tion. For the Martian photographs in this volume I should like again to express my gratitude to them all.

To the many individuals who aided in the preparation of this book I want here to extend my public thanks. A special acknowledgment is due to Dr. John S. Hall, Director, and to the staff of the Lowell Observatory who have at all times been helpful in too many ways to detail.

E. C. Slipher
December 23, 1963

CONTENTS

LIST OF PLATES

JUPITER

SATURN

Explanation of Data on Plates

The longitudes of the central meridians (λ) for both Mars and Jupiter were computed from the values tabulated in the American Ephemeris and Nautical Almanac in the section designated as Ephemeris for Physical Observations. For Jupiter, System II was used.

The Martian date (M.D.) indicates the season with an accuracy of one or two days. It can be ambiguous because it is possible to calculate it for either Martian hemisphere. Except for those few cases when attention is drawn to the "autumn" or North Pole of the planet, the Martian date applies only to its southern hemisphere. The Martian seasons, however, always correspond to the seasons experienced by an observer in the northern hemisphere of the Earth.

The general procedure for the calculation of the M.D. is as follows: The Ephemeris for Physical Observations of Mars in the *Nautical Almanac* (Part IV) contains the longitude of the Sun as seen from Mars for each alternate Earth day of the year as measured from the Martian vernal equinox. One looks up the longitude of the Sun as seen from Mars for the ephemeris date of observation, and subtracts 180° from the longitude (to obtain dates for the Martian southern hemisphere corresponding to our calendar for Earth's northern hemisphere). The table of the Sun's longitude (counted from our vernal equinox) as a function of date in Part I of the Ephemeris is then scanned to match the longitude just determined and the corresponding date is found. This date is the southern hemisphere Martian date. To obtain the Martian date for the Martian northern hemisphere, corresponding to our calendar, one omits the subtraction of 180°.

In the study of the planets it is imperative to know their relation to the Sun, since solar radiation is the primary cause of visible surface change. Therefore, it is vital to recognize the points where radiation begins, its duration, and where it ends; these are the points of sunrise and sunset. All the photographs here are arranged with the South Pole at the top and since the planets all rotate from west to east like the Sun, the prints are oriented in such a way that east, or sunset, is to the left, and that west, or sunrise, is to the right.

Naturally during the long period covered by the photographs in this book there have been advantageous technological changes in plates and filters which have resulted in shorter exposure times. In the early part of the century low-sensitivity emulsions were common and the planetary image had to be quite small in order to permit short exposure times. As faster plates became available, the focal length of the camera and the image sizes were increased accordingly. In the early days the amplifying lens of the camera was set to give an equivalent focal length of 150—175 feet, resulting in original Mars images of 4—5 mm in diameter, and an exposure time of 2 to 3 seconds. The images of Jupiter and Saturn were from 9—12 mm, with an exposure time of 6—8 seconds for Jupiter, and 20—30 seconds for Saturn. Obviously, for such long exposures the seeing had to be excellent to produce sharp images. Within the last 25 years newer emulsions have become available that are 25—30 times faster in the green, yellow, orange and red. These plates possess reasonably fine grain, and are of great benefit to the planetary photographer because cameras of over 225 feet focal length can be used. In the case of Mars, images 7—8 mm in size are now photographed in 1/20—1/25 of a second under favorable conditions, Jupiter ¾ of a second, and Saturn 1½—3 seconds. In addition to the improvement in photographic emulsions and color filters over the years, new precision enlargers have been developed for optically superimposing many negative images from a single plate into one composite image. More details pertinent to planetary photography are given in Chapter VI in the book on Mars.

Doubtless the reader would like to know how the magnification of our photographs, as they appear here, compares in scale with that generally seen visually in large telescopes. Because of the ever-changing distances of the planets as they swing around the Sun, it is not feasible to give specific magnifications for all the photographs but it may suffice to say that as viewed at normal vision of ten inches all the planets appear here as large or larger than as generally observed visually in large telescopes. That is they appear as if magnified several hundred diameters at least, (the power generally used visually) and up to 1800 times in the case of the Mars photograph No. 2 in Plate XXXI, and equal to 2,150 in the case of No. 4 in Plate XXXII. In the case of Jupiter the photograph in Plate XLIII is equivalent to a magnification of 1,250 and in the case of Saturn in Plate LVIII, the greater enlargements show the planet as if magnified 1,600 diameters. (The foregoing magnifications were derived from the photographs appearing in the general edition, but since the size of the images in the limited edition is about ten percent smaller these magnifications should be reduced by a corresponding amount.)

For data on the resolving power of a photographic plate and the smallest marking possible to record photographically on Mars, refer to the author's earlier book[1].

With the development of spectroscopic emulsions in recent years, it is now possible, with proper filters and plates, to secure separate "monochromatic" photographs of the brighter planets for every 500 —800 angstroms of the spectrum from $\lambda 3600$ to $\lambda 11,500$. (See Plate VI of Venus.) Table I shows the approximate effective wavelengths used for the photographs in this book.

[1]Slipher, E. C., 1962, *The Photographic Story of Mars*, pp. 58 and 59.

TABLE I

Approximate Effective Wavelengths and Symbols Used to Represent Them.

SYMBOL	RANGE (ANGSTROMS)	FILTER OR PLATES	REMARKS
UV	3650—4000	UG-2	Blue corrector
B	4000—5000	Lantern Plates III-O Plates	Blue corrector
G	4700—5250	Wr 8 or 11 J Plates	———
Y	5000—5850	Wr 12	———
O	5500—6250	Wr 16	———
R	6000—6700	Wr 29F	———
IR	7600—12000	N to Z	IR corrector

PLATES

Plate I

In Plate I, images 1 and 2 are exquisite little photographs of Jupiter (Common, 1879) and of Saturn (Henry brothers, 1885). These were among the first direct photographs of a planet showing recognizable surface markings. Both were made on blue-sensitive plates (because orthochromatic emulsions were then unobtainable) with telescopes corrected in the blue. The first picture, showing the Red Spot conspicuous in the southern (upper) hemisphere and a single prominent belt across the equatorial region of Jupiter, emphasizes the redness of the Red Spot by showing it extremely dark in blue light. That of Saturn shows a dark cap at the south pole, a dark belt in the tropics, and a dark sash across the equator. The picture further reveals that the whole ball was then reddish in color, because it was so much darker than the ring system in blue light. This spectacular darkening of the ball is further illustrated in Plate LXI.

The upper Lowell photograph of March 22, 1948, is a direct copy of the best single image on a Saturn negative; below it is a composite made from 10 images of the same negative. Graininess has been greatly reduced by the multiplying process and the more salient markings, such as the zones and belts, have been smoothed out and greatly enhanced in visibility but with some sacrifice in sharpness. However, the advantages outweigh the disadvantages.

Approximate ranges in wavelength which apply to the various color symbols used in this book are described in Table I. As different color filters, telescopes and plates were used throughout the years, the wavelength limits might be slightly different.

2

PLATE I

EARLY PHOTOGRAPHS OF JUPITER AND SATURN

Sept. 3, 1879 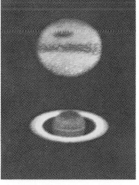 A. A. COMMON

Dec. 21, 1885 Paul and Prosper
Henry

"History of Astronomy During
the Nineteenth Century",
Agnes M. Clerke

PHOTOGRAPHS OF SATURN

March 22, 1948

SINGLE IMAGE

TEN IMAGE COMPOSITE OF SAME PLATE

Plate II

Mercury is by far the most difficult of all the brighter planets to catch on the photographic plate. The exposure time required to register its image shows that its albedo is about that of our Moon, which, in some respects, it resembles. The low albedo and the small disk of the planet make it far more difficult than Venus to photograph against the daylight sky, a procedure made necessary by its close proximity to the Sun. If one chooses to photograph in the twilight hours, the advantage gained by the darker sky is more than lost by poor seeing owing to the planet's low altitude; consequently, useful photographs of Mercury are extremely rare. Attempts at Flagstaff to secure first-class tri-color photographs have been disappointing, but enough has been obtained in red, yellow, and blue light to demonstrate that there is no appreciable difference in the appearance of the disk in these regions of the spectrum. The uniformity of color and brightness across the whole disk strongly indicates the absence of haze, clouds or any detectable atmosphere.

Slipher (1938)[1] pointed out that the markings on Mercury are faint, diffuse, and irregular in shape and arrangement, and that the unchanging surface appearace resembles that of our Moon. It is very puzzling that some observers have repeatedly reported seeing on Mercury white spots or haze which temporarily concealed the surface markings. Although our photographs of this planet are inferior to our best negatives of Mars, the definition of the Mercury plates is sufficient to reveal haze and clouds if they are as conspicuous as described by Antoniadi (1934)[2]; "The haze on Mercury is whitish; it occurs more frequently and is denser than that on Mars." Our observations and tri-color photographs reveal no evidence of any haze or clouds, or of any sensible atmosphere. In fact, the low albedo of the planet, comparable to that of the Moon is consistent with this conclusion. Visual observations show stationary markings on the apparent disk; therefore, the period of rotation and revolution are equal.

[1]Slipher, E. C., 1938, P.A.S.P., *9*, 167.
[2]Antoniadi, E. M., 1930, La Planēte Mars

4

PLATE II

MERCURY 1934

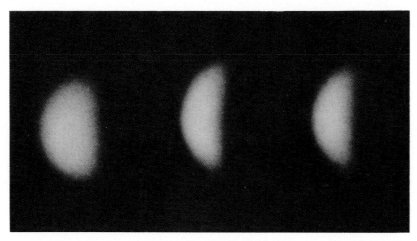

June 7   June 11   June 12

Plate III

Plate III shows daylight photographs of Venus in five different phases taken through a yellow color filter. These are part of the photographic record of this planet which began at Flagstaff in 1904. The yellow-filter photographs, even of highest quality, have never shown anything but faint, irregular markings on the disk and, occasionally, polar caps which are merely brighter than the surrounding regions. When the planet is in the crescent phase, both the yellow and deep-red photographs have displayed extensions of the horns of the crescent beyond the geometric semicircle. These extensions are produced by the impenetrable atmosphere on Venus. See also Plate IV.

6

PLATE III

VENUS 1919

YELLOW PHOTOGRAPHS SHOWING FIVE DIFFERENT PHASES

Plate IV

Plate IV shows a series of photographs of Venus taken through a Wratten 70 filter on November 19–22, 1938, and June 24, 25, 1940, near inferior conjunction. Within about one day of conjunction a complete ring can be seen around the dark disk due to the illuminated atmosphere of Venus. Near conjunction very unequal atmospheric prolongations of the horns of the crescent were observed, the southern one being persistently longer than the northern by 45 to 50 degrees. On November 22 a reddish cloud about 700 miles long was repeatedly recorded in the twilight arc about 30 degrees from the tip of the sunlit crescent[1].

Over 500 tri-color photographs made near inferior conjunction showing the atmospheric ring provided excellent material for determining the diameter of Venus free of irradiation and systematic errors by directly measuring the size of the dark disk inside the atmospheric ring. The weighted mean of the red, yellow and blue images gave 7617 miles for the diameter of Venus.

Other measures of the photographs showed: (1) the brightness of the twilight on Venus was, at the brightest point, thirty times that of the sky near the sun; (2) the color of the twilight was bluish, the brightness being four times stronger in blue than in red light; the cloud mass (bright condensation in twilight Nov. 22) was reddish, being invisible in blue and conspicuous in red photographs; (3) the height of the upper atmosphere of Venus involved in these twilight phenomena varied from about 700 to 25,000 feet; (4) the sunlight reached us through the planet's atmosphere chiefly by reflection and not by refraction; (5) measures of the dark disk of Venus showed the same brightness as the adjacent sky.

At Table Mountain, California, Edson, Wright, Winget and Canright[2] (1940) obtained about 1800 ultraviolet, blue, yellow, red, and infrared photographs of Venus which showed no appreciable differences between the five different wave bands. In all five colors there was the same basic atmospheric pattern; the height distribution in 1940 was the same as observed at the 1938 conjunction, namely an extremely high atmospheric scattering over the southern cusp and a smaller maximum over the northern cusp. Similar inequalities were observed by Slipher at the 1919 and 1954 conjunctions, suggesting that this peculiar distribution of atmosphere above the opaque layer of Venus is permanent, and as Edson thought, related to the planet's winds and axial rotation.

---

[1]Slipher, E. C., and Edson, J. B., 1938, P.A.S.P., *9*, 229; 1939, Sky, *3*, 3.
[2]Edson, J. B., Wright, E. B., Winget, J. L., and Canright, R. B., 1940, Pub. A.A.S., *10,* 25

8

PLATE IV

VENUS AT INFERIOR CONJUNCTION

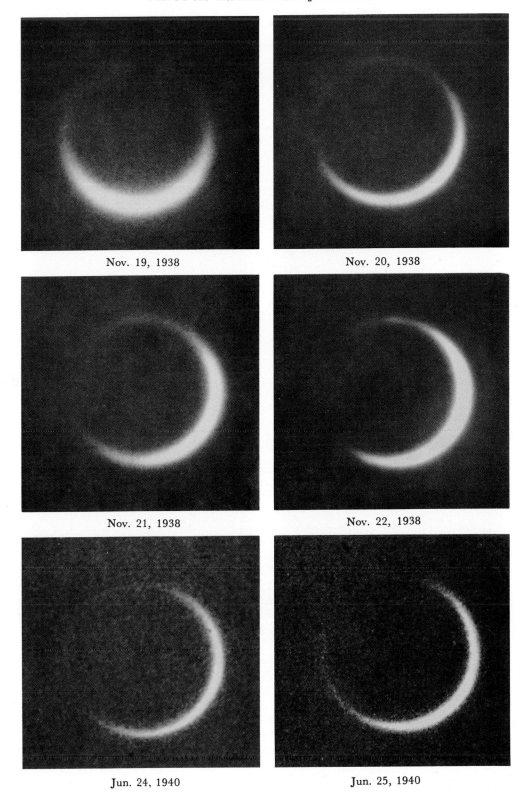

Nov. 19, 1938   Nov. 20, 1938

Nov. 21, 1938   Nov. 22, 1938

Jun. 24, 1940   Jun. 25, 1940

Plate V

Plate V shows nearly simultaneous red, yellow and blue photographs of Venus on November 22, 1938, when the planet was two days past inferior conjunction. Values found for the diameter of Venus measured in red, green and blue were 7610, 7628 and 7637 miles respectively.

All the early efforts to photograph Venus at Flagstaff (from 1904 on) concentrated on attempts to record the markings by penetrating the atmosphere of the planet at longer wavelengths. The method succeeded in registering only faint vague markings too weak to add new information. Visually, faint gray shadings showed on the disk at times, with brighter polar caps sometimes outlined by a dusky collar.

Quenisset[1] (1913) reported that he had recorded faint, but certain spots on seven violet photographs of Venus taken with a small astrographic objective at the Flammarion Observatory at Juvisy. He described the spots as grayish, very faint and diffuse. As the photographs were too small for reproduction, he published a drawing made from the plate.

[1]Quenisset, F., 1913, L'Astronomie, *27*, 2, 53.

PLATE V

VENUS AT INFERIOR CONJUNCTION NOV. 22, 1938

TRI-COLOR PHOTOGRAPHS OF THE RING

RED

YELLOW

BLUE

Plate VI

Plate VI shows a series of ten photographs of Venus taken in various spectral regions (U.V. to I.R., $\lambda3650$–$\lambda12000$). The object of this survey was to find a possible window in the atmosphere of Venus. No new spectral regions in which the planet's atmosphere was transparent were found and no new markings appeared on the photographs except a small dark spot near the terminator shown on the Z plate, which was not confirmed because of the long exposure required—16 minutes. It is mentioned here on the chance someone may be encouraged to again try to obtain photographs in this region of the spectrum.

12

PLATE VI
MONOCHROMATIC PHOTOGRAPHS OF VENUS IN TEN SEPARATE
REGIONS OF THE SPECTRUM FROM λ3650 TO λ12000.

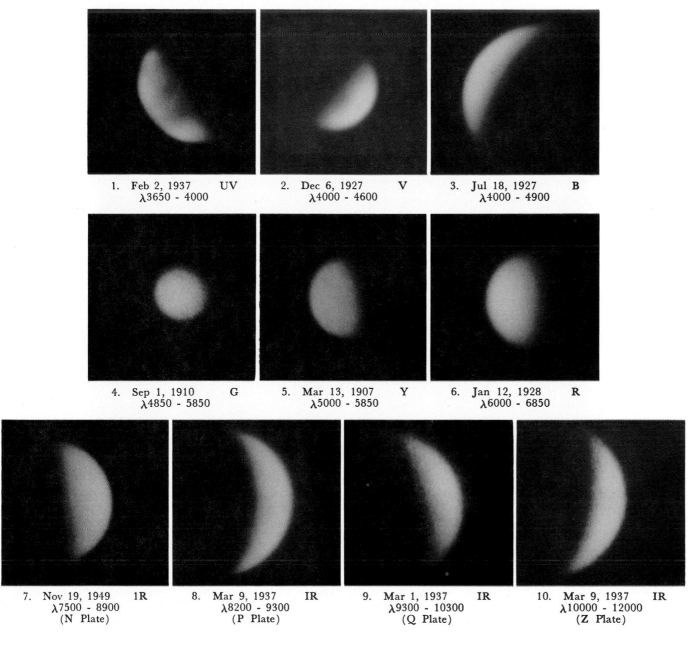

1. Feb 2, 1937 UV λ3650 - 4000	2. Dec 6, 1927 V λ4000 - 4600	3. Jul 18, 1927 B λ4000 - 4900
4. Sep 1, 1910 G λ4850 - 5850	5. Mar 13, 1907 Y λ5000 - 5850	6. Jan 12, 1928 R λ6000 - 6850

7. Nov 19, 1949   1R
λ7500 - 8900
(N Plate)

8. Mar 9, 1937   IR
λ8200 - 9300
(P Plate)

9. Mar 1, 1937   IR
λ9300 - 10300
(Q Plate)

10. Mar 9, 1937   IR
λ10000 - 12000
(Z Plate)

Plate VII

Plate VII shows twenty-five ultraviolet photographs of Venus taken by the author between 1928 and 1948. These images were chosen to show the whole variety of bright and dark areas of the planet; sometimes the polar regions are strikingly bright and at other times they appear unusually dark but most often the mid-portion of the disk is dominated by dark, irregular belts. The dark markings are generally strongest at the terminator and tend to run in belts approximately perpendicular to it. Note that on June 13, 1935, the two photographs taken at U.T. 2:57 and 21:57 appear to show noticeable changes in the principal markings. The first of these photographs (No. 12) shows the southern horn very dark, also an exceedingly bright area lower down the disk; whereas the later one (No. 13) exhibits a bright cap which covers the southern horn, while the other principal markings have changed form and position.

Some observers who have published ultraviolet photographs of this planet have referred only to dark belts as the chief feature of the disk. Certainly the unmatched series of photographs by Ross in 1927[1] and later photographs by Richardson (1954)[2] emphasize the predominance of dark belts as the characteristic feature of the disk. On the contrary the dominant feature of a photograph by Wright in 1924[3] and the only one he described was a broad bright band across the disk. Most of our UV photographs in 1928, 1929 and 1931 reveal that the most conspicuous markings were large irregular bright areas, often covering a large portion of the central part of the disk. From comparisons with intensity scales impressed on the plates these bright areas were sometimes nearly twice as bright as the darkest part of the disk. These bright areas are pointed out to show that vast changes in the cloud cover take place in some years, although more often than not dark belt-like features predominate. The manner in which all the markings merge gradually into one another suggest an atmospheric origin, and the best explanation of the observations is that the upper surface consists of billowy clouds some of which tower above others to the extent of some miles.

There is considerable evidence that there is some relationship between the visual and photographic markings. Certainly the bright cap at the top and bottom of many of the photographs[1] must represent the same bright "polar caps" often seen by Lowell and others at Flagstaff in the earlier years (1906-1911). These phenomena, often clearly seen, looked like polar caps, the southern one being the most conspicuous. They were not white like those on Mars but were the same color as the disk, only brighter, and the southern one is usually outlined by sort of a vague darkish collar. Usually to me vague irregular grayish markings also appeared on the disk which, in spite of their spotted appearance, often appeared streaky, becoming most noticeable at the terminator. Thus, there is considerable evidence that there is some relationship between certain of the visual observations and the photographic markings on Venus, but the agreement in the case of the dark markings is not very convincing.

[1]Ross, Frank E., 1928, Ap.J., *68,* 62, (see plates I and II).
[2]Richardson, R. S., 1955, P.A.S.P., *67,* 304.
[3]Wright, W. H., 1927, P.A.S.P., *39,* 220

PLATE VII
TYPICAL ULTRAVIOLET PHOTOGRAPHS (λ3650 TO 4000) TAKEN FROM 1927 TO 1948
DISPLAYING VARIATIONS IN THE CLOUD COVER ON VENUS

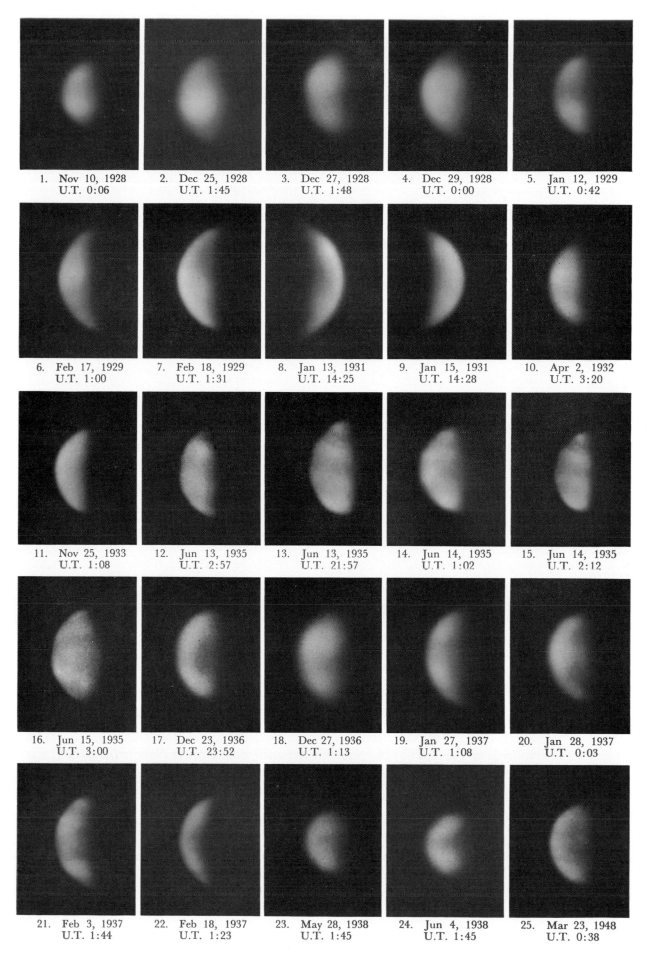

1. Nov 10, 1928
    U.T. 0:06

2. Dec 25, 1928
    U.T. 1:45

3. Dec 27, 1928
    U.T. 1:48

4. Dec 29, 1928
    U.T. 0:00

5. Jan 12, 1929
    U.T. 0:42

6. Feb 17, 1929
    U.T. 1:00

7. Feb 18, 1929
    U.T. 1:31

8. Jan 13, 1931
    U.T. 14:25

9. Jan 15, 1931
    U.T. 14:28

10. Apr 2, 1932
    U.T. 3:20

11. Nov 25, 1933
    U.T. 1:08

12. Jun 13, 1935
    U.T. 2:57

13. Jun 13, 1935
    U.T. 21:57

14. Jun 14, 1935
    U.T. 1:02

15. Jun 14, 1935
    U.T. 2:12

16. Jun 15, 1935
    U.T. 3:00

17. Dec 23, 1936
    U.T. 23:52

18. Dec 27, 1936
    U.T. 1:13

19. Jan 27, 1937
    U.T. 1:08

20. Jan 28, 1937
    U.T. 0:03

21. Feb 3, 1937
    U.T. 1:44

22. Feb 18, 1937
    U.T. 1:23

23. May 28, 1938
    U.T. 1:45

24. Jun 4, 1938
    U.T. 1:45

25. Mar 23, 1948
    U.T. 0:38

Plate VIII

This photograph, taken December 4, 1911, only a few days after opposition, shows the disk of Mars just before occultation by the moon. It reveals that, even at a better-than-average opposition, the planet's apparent disk is no larger in area than a medium-to-small crater on the moon. This serves to emphasize the meticulous care necessary to discover the hundreds of details that have been recorded on Mars and which confirm the numerous changes that have been observed. The photograph also demonstrates the nearly equal surface brightness of the two objects.

16

PLATE VIII

OCCULTATION OF MARS BY THE MOON

OCCULTATION OF MARS BY THE MOON

Plate IX

The maps shown in Plates IX and X were compiled by the author and based largely on many drawings made by Percival Lowell and the author. Photographs of the principal regions of Mars are also shown above each map to facilitate identification of features. The nomenclature is based primarily on Schiaparelli's (1877-1884) and differs in a few cases from that adopted in 1958 by the International Astronomical Union. Some I.A.U. spellings for names of features are shown in parentheses. In following the legends pertinent to Mars plates the reader may wish to identify markings by referring to the map and the list of features tabulated below.

The reader will note the positions of the points of compass (see also Introduction).

Adamas	A2	Lacus Phoenicis	D3
Aethiopis	A2	Laestrygon	A3
Aethiops	A2	Laestrygonum Sinus	A3
Agathodaemon	C3	Libya	A2
Amenthes	A2	Libya-Syrtis	B2
Aquae Calidae	A1	Lucus Moeris	B2
Argyre I	C4	Maeisia Silva	C3
Arsia Silva	D3	Mare Acidalium	C1
Astaboras	B2	Mare Australe	B4 C4
Astusapes	B2	Mare Cimmerium	A3
Atlantis	D3	Mare Erythraeum	C3
Aurora Sinus	C3	Mare Sirenum	D3
Bathys	D3	Mare Tyrrhenum	A3
Biblis Fons	D2	Margaritifer Sinus	C3
Casius	A1	Meridiani Sinus	B3
Cimmerium	A3	Mts. of Mitchel	B4
Corax	C3	Nectar	C3
Daemon	C3	Nepenthes-Thoth	A2
Dawes Bay	B3	Noachis	B3
Deucalion	B3	Nodus Lacoontis	A2
Deucalionis R.	B3	Nuba Lacus	A2
Eden	B2	Ophir	C3
Elysium	A2	Pandorae Fretum	B3
Eumenides	D3	Phoenicis Lacus	D3
Eunostos	A2	Poras	A3
Euphrates	B2	Sabaeus Sinus	B3
Fastigium Aryn	B2	Sinus Gomer	A3
Ferentinae Lacus	D2	Solis Lacus	C3
Gehon	C2	Syrtis Major	B2
Hadriaticum	B3	Tharsis	D3
Hellas	B4	Thaumasia	C3
Hellespontus	B4	Thoth	A2
Hesperia Strait	A3	Thoth-Nepenthes	A2
Hydraotes	C2	Thoth-Nepenthes-Triton	A2
Ionium	B3	Tithonius	C3
Isidis-Libya	A2	Tithonius Lacus	C3
Isidis Regio	A2	Ulysses	D2
Jamuna Canal	C2		

18

PLATE IX
REFERENCE MAP OF MARS AND ASSOCIATED PHOTOGRAPHS OF PRINCIPAL REGIONS.

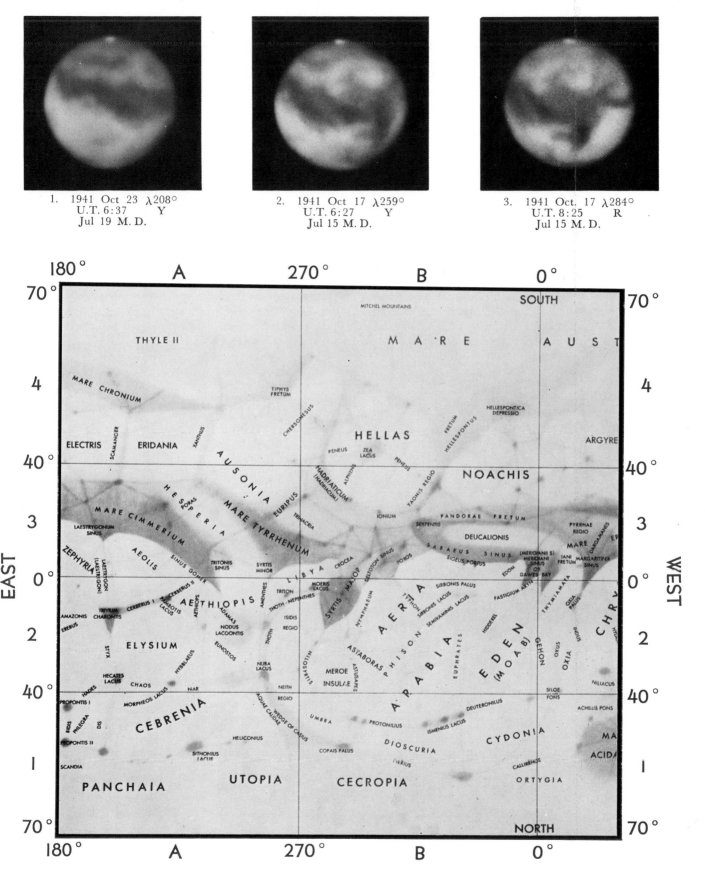

1. 1941 Oct 23 λ208°
U.T. 6:37   Y
Jul 19 M.D.

2. 1941 Oct 17 λ259°
U.T. 6:27   Y
Jul 15 M.D.

3. 1941 Oct. 17 λ284°
U.T. 8:25   R
Jul 15 M.D.

Plate X

Description of map is given in legend for Plate IX.

Adamas	A2	Lacus Phoenicis		D3
Aethiopis	A2	Laestrygon		A3
Aethiops	A2	Laestrygonum Sinus		A3
Agathodaemon	C3	Libya		A2
Amenthes	A2	Libya-Syrtis		B2
Aquae Calidae	A1	Lucus Moeris		B2
Argyre I	C4	Maeisia Silva		C3
Arsia Silva	D3	Mare Acidalium		C1
Astaboras	B2	Mare Australe	B4	C4
Astusapes	B2	Mare Cimmerium		A3
Atlantis	D3	Mare Erythraeum		C3
Aurora Sinus	C3	Mare Sirenum		D3
Bathys	D3	Mare Tyrrhenum		A3
Biblis Fons	D2	Margaritifer Sinus		C3
Casius	A1	Meridiani Sinus		B3
Cimmerium	A3	Mts. of Mitchel		B4
Corax	C3	Nectar		C3
Daemon	C3	Nepenthes-Thoth		A2
Dawes Bay	B3	Noachis		B3
Deucalion	B3	Nodus Lacoontis		A2
Deucalionis R.	B3	Nuba Lacus		A2
Eden	B2	Ophir		C3
Elysium	A2	Pandorae Fretum		B3
Eumenides	D3	Phoenicis Lacus		D3
Eunostos	A2	Poras		A3
Euphrates	B2	Sabaeus Sinus		B3
Fastigium Aryn	B2	Sinus Gomer		A3
Ferentinae Lacus	D2	Solis Lacus		C3
Gehon	C2	Syrtis Major		B2
Hadriaticum	B3	Tharsis		D3
Hellas	B4	Thaumasia		C3
Hellespontus	B4	Thoth		A2
Hesperia Strait	A3	Thoth-Nepenthes		A2
Hydraotes	C2	Thoth-Nepenthes-Triton		A2
Ionium	B3	Tithonius		C3
Isidis-Libya	A2	Tithonius Lacus		C3
Isidis Regio	A2	Ulysses		D2
Jamuna Canal	C2			

20

PLATE X

REFERENCE MAP OF MARS AND ASSOCIATED PHOTOGRAPHS OF PRINCIPAL REGIONS.

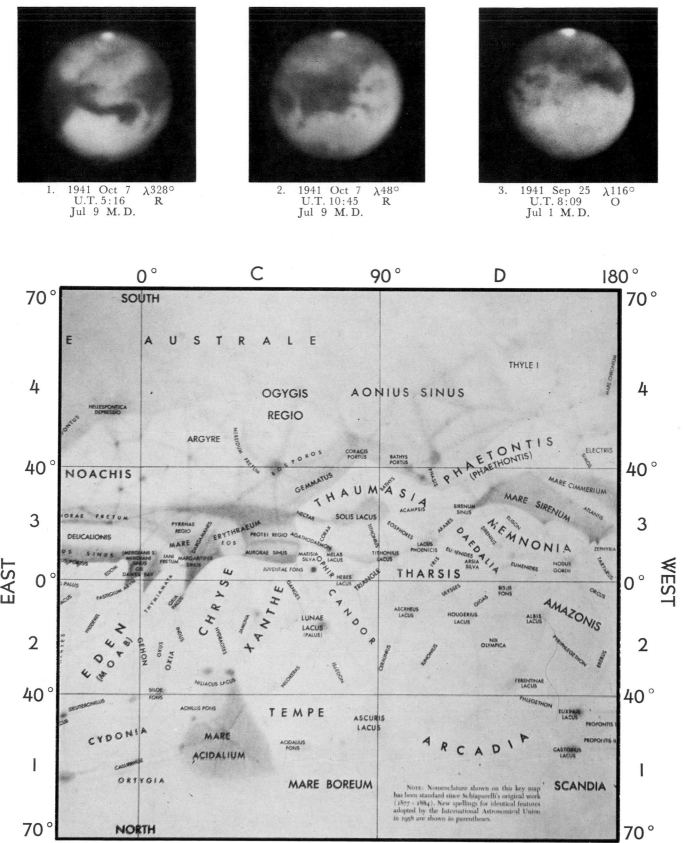

1. 1941 Oct 7 λ328°
U.T. 5:16   R
Jul 9 M.D.

2. 1941 Oct 7 λ48°
U.T. 10:45   R
Jul 9 M.D.

3. 1941 Sep 25 λ116°
U.T. 8:09   O
Jul 1 M.D.

NOTE: Nomenclature shown on this key map has been standard since Schiaparelli's original work (1877 - 1884). New spellings for identical features adopted by the International Astronomical Union in 1958 are shown in parentheses.

Plate XI

In 1907 Mars was more favorably placed for observation than it had been for more than a dozen years. The distance at opposition was 38,500,000 miles, not far from its smallest possible value. However, Mars was 25° south of the equator during the favorable time for observations; therefore it was unfavorably low in the southern sky for good observations from northern sites. Lowell, inspired by the initial success in photographing some the canals at Flagstaff in 1905[1], and anxious to make full use of the next favorable opposition to continue the work, sent an expedition[2] to the Andes to observe Mars where it would culminate near the zenith each night. Fortunate in obtaining the loan of the excellent 18-inch refractor of Amherst College, the expedition set out from New York, by way of Panama on May 11 for an outdoor station at Alianza, Chile. The station was situated on the Tarapaca desert, elevation 4000 feet, in south latitude 20°30′, and inland about 70 miles from Iquique and beyond the coast range of the Andes. Here in this rainless and almost cloudless desert waste, the seeing was exceptionally fine.

The accompanying photographs are representative examples from over 13,000 taken by the expedition. They have been prepared by optically superimposing about a half-dozen images from each plate into one composite picture, in order to minimize the effect of plate grain, but at the cost of losing much of the finer detail. Here the photographs are arranged in order of Martian longitudes of the disk, and cover one complete circuit of the planet. Although not of serious consequence, it should be noted that some of the times on this plate were not accurately recorded, owing to difficulties of observing at a temporary outdoor isolated station.

The photgraphs show among other things: 1) temporary mists and clouds obscuring dark regions, (see veiled dark regions in Nos. 12 and 14); 2) night-to-night disappearance and reappearance of the canopy at the north pole demonstrating it consisted then chiefly of cloud; 3) the slow, gradual shrinking of the south cap with its fixed dark rifts and bright spots, revealing that it was a fixed deposit on the solid surface as contrasted with the cloud character of the north cap; 4) the temporary clouds in Southern Tharsis region near Lacus Phoenicis (these clouds have been much observed in later years especially in 1926 and 1954 when the configuration was referred to as the "W" cloud group); 5) morning limblight preceding Syrtis Major (see No. 20); and 6) definite traces of the majority of all canals shown in 108 complete drawings made from visual observations during the same period. On some of the best images, the original plates show as many as twenty-six of these delicate lines and oases. The Gehon, which was strong in 1907, and the Euphrates were shown to be double beyond doubt. This early series of photographs, supplemented by 4000 to 5000 secured at Flagstaff, have proved of great value in providing comparisons with later photographs. Note the unusual visibility of the Nilotis canal leading northward from the Syrtis Major in Nos. 17 and 18 (See Plate IX, B2), a canal seen first in 1856 and photographed at Flagstaff at each opposition since 1905, yet it is unexplainably omitted from the official map of the I. A. U. and its list of Martian markings.

---

[1]Lowell, P., 1905, Lowell Obs. Bull., *1*, 21.

[2]Members of the Expedition included Dr. David P. Todd, in charge; Mrs. Todd; A. G. Ilse, engineer of the Alvan Clark Corp.; R. G. Eaglesfield, electrician and general assistant; and the writer as observer.

PLATE XI
1907 CIRCUIT OF MARS

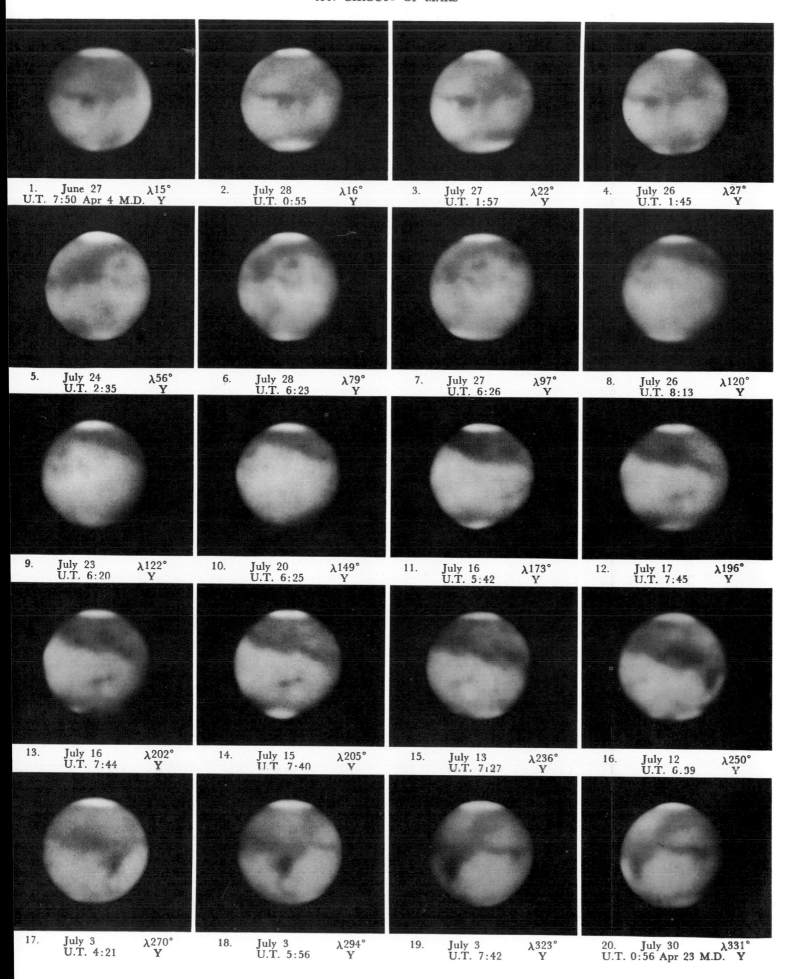

1. June 27 λ15° U.T. 7:50 Apr 4 M.D. Y	2. July 28 λ16° U.T. 0:55 Y	3. July 27 λ22° U.T. 1:57 Y	4. July 26 λ27° U.T. 1:45 Y
5. July 24 λ56° U.T. 2:35 Y	6. July 28 λ79° U.T. 6:23 Y	7. July 27 λ97° U.T. 6:26 Y	8. July 26 λ120° U.T. 8:13 Y
9. July 23 λ122° U.T. 6:20 Y	10. July 20 λ149° U.T. 6:25 Y	11. July 16 λ173° U.T. 5:42 Y	12. July 17 λ196° U.T. 7:45 Y
13. July 16 λ202° U.T. 7:44 Y	14. July 15 λ205° U.T. 7:40 Y	15. July 13 λ236° U.T. 7:27 Y	16. July 12 λ250° U.T. 6:39 Y
17. July 3 λ270° U.T. 4:21 Y	18. July 3 λ294° U.T. 5:56 Y	19. July 3 λ323° U.T. 7:42 Y	20. July 30 λ331° U.T. 0:56 Apr 23 M.D. Y

Plate XII

Following the initial efforts at Flagstaff to secure successful photographs of the planet in yellow light from 1903 to 1907, attempts to obtain photographs in other regions of the spectrum were begun in 1909 by making tri-color exposures in red, green and blue. The first row of images shows early examples of such tri-color photographs made in 1909. Results with the 42-inch reflector disclosed the surprising observations that blue images were completely blank, showed none of the permanent dark markings, and yet clearly enhanced the cloud cap and cloud areas. The green tri-color filter, which passed both green and blue light, (compensated filters were then not available) recorded the surface markings weakly as compared to the redder image which showed these in strongest contrast. Since similar tri-color photographs of paintings by Howard Russell Butler, N. A. gave identical results (second row), it was reasonable at that time to conclude that the explanation lay in the effect of selective reflection between the blue-green dark areas and the reddish deserts. This resulted in a complete leveling-out of the two in the blue photographs; the thought was that the thin atmosphere of Mars could have little or no effect.

The cause of the disappearance of the surface markings on the blue photographs, however, is less simple—there are at least two possibilities. One is that the actual colors of the reddish surface of the planet and its greenish-gray markings are such that in red light the first is much brighter than the second, while in blue light the red has lost much of its brightness and little contrast remains. The other is that the atmosphere of Mars, though transparent to red and fairly so to yellow, is very thick and hazy to blue light, and hence obscures the surface details.

No definite conclusion between these two alternatives seemed possible until 1937[1], when photographs by the writer revealed a state of blue clearing on May 20-23 so striking that the blue images revealed the surface details almost as clearly as ordinary yellow photographs. This example of blue clearing in the atmosphere of Mars led to the verification of others, both before and since, with the result that the explanation of the *"violet layer"* and its temporary clearings has become a much discussed problem. A considerable number of explanations have been offered by physicists and physical chemists but none of these is free from serious objection.

The last row of images shows typical examples of modern tri-color photographs when the atmosphere of Mars was opaque to violet light. It is important to note here that there is no limb darkening in the blue photograph. Limb darkening is the fundamental requirement of the new theory announced recently by Öpik[2] that carbon monoxide in the Martian atmosphere accounts for the violet layer.

[1]Slipher, E. C., 1937, P.A.S.P., *49*, 289, p. 137.
[2]Öpik, E. J., 1960, J. of Geo. Res., *65*, 10, p. 3057.

PLATE XII
EARLY TRI-COLOR EXPERIMENTS

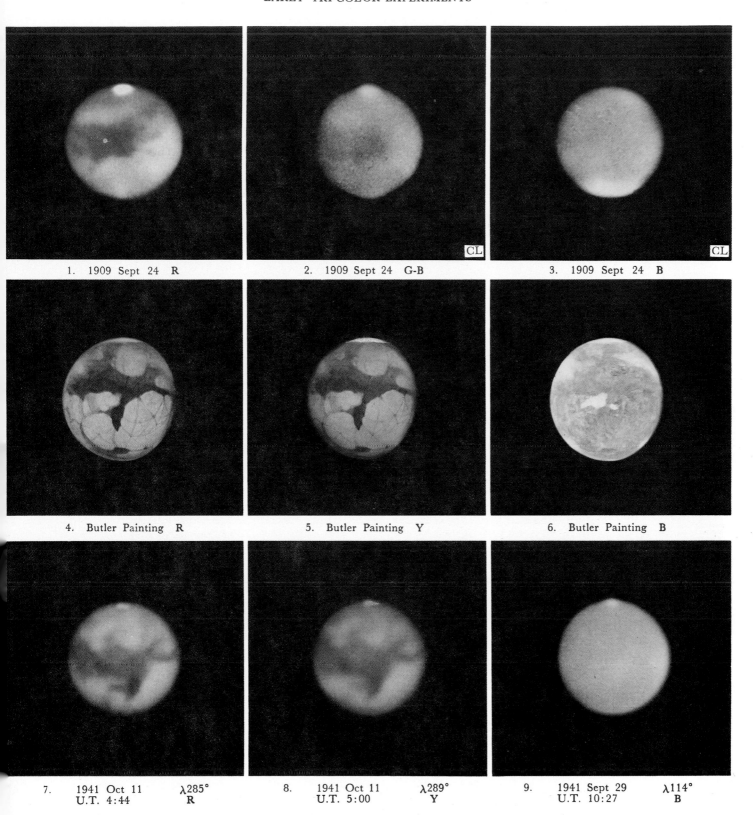

1. 1909 Sept 24 R   2. 1909 Sept 24 G-B   3. 1909 Sept 24 B

4. Butler Painting R   5. Butler Painting Y   6. Butler Painting B

7.   1941 Oct 11   λ285°   8.   1941 Oct 11   λ289°   9.   1941 Sept 29   λ114°
    U.T. 4:44   R   U.T. 5:00   Y   U.T. 10:27   B

Plate XIII

Typical examples of yellow photographs from 1905 to 1928 show changes of various features over the Syrtis Major region of Mars. Most of these changes are so self-evident that they hardly need description. However, attention may be called to some of the more outstanding ones. First note the great difference between the 1907 and 1909 photographs where the former in its springtime shows the maria (Mare Tyrrhenum, Ionium, Hadriaticum, Hellespontus) and Hellas as a rather uniform gray up to the south cap. In Martian summer in 1909, however, these same features have strikingly darkened, but the Hellas and the islands preceding it have definitely brightened. In 1909 the Syrtis itself appears narrower than in 1907, but the Lucus Moeris shows extensive development in the preceding direction, although the Thoth was even fainter than at the previous opposition. In 1911 to 1920 especially, the Thoth and other desert features developed considerable strength. In 1918 the Syrtis appears appreciably smaller and weaker as compared to its strength in 1920 and 1922. In 1922 dense yellow clouds appeared over Hellas with a faint fringe reaching well down toward the southern Syrtis at times. In 1924 the Syrtis again became abnormally narrow but the maria again show considerable darkening (Martian date May 17). The Thoth was again darker in 1926. In 1928 it became one of the grosser features of the disk and dark markings developed strongly in the Aethiops region. Aside from these major changes many minor ones occurred in this period.

Especially noteworthy here are the many variations in the appearance in the Hellas as shown in Plates XIII and XIV. Sometimes, as in 1909, it is large and bright, then at the next opposition in 1911 it is unevenly dark. The photographs also show that it rarely, if ever, appears exactly the same at any two oppositions, and that most often it appears brighter in Martian spring and summer which suggests that the increase in brightness may be due to dust and clouds.

The virtual disappearance of the Thoth in 1909, coupled with its strong development at the later oppositions, clearly suggests that it is not a permanent feature but is due to something which develops on the surface.

26

PLATE XIII

CHANGES IN THE CANALS AND DARK MARKINGS NEAR THE SYRTIS MAJOR REGION — 1905-1928.

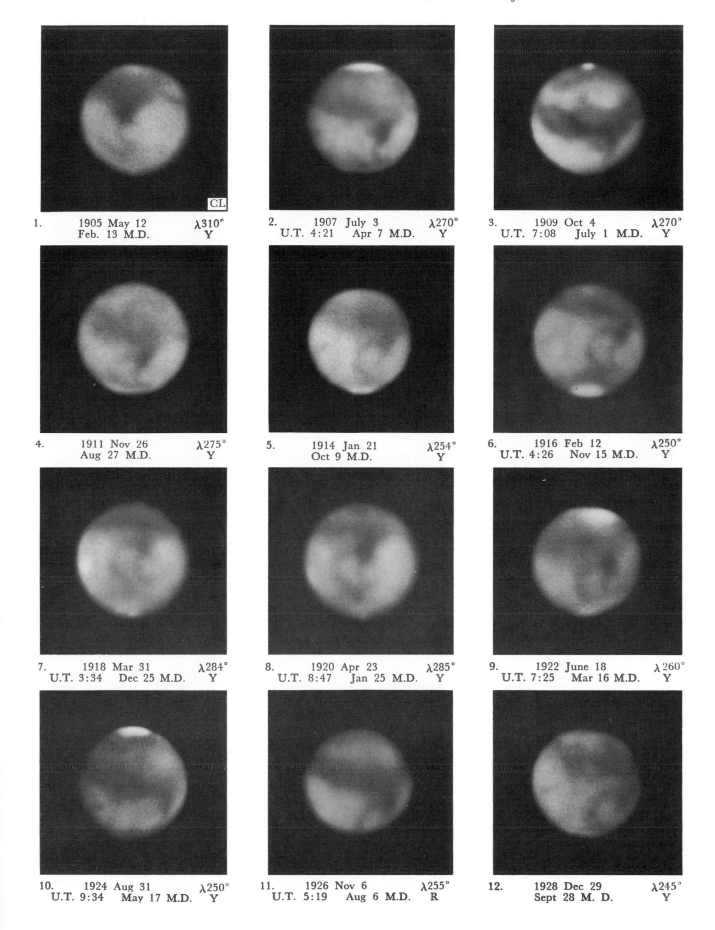

1. 1905 May 12 λ310° Feb. 13 M.D. Y	2. 1907 July 3 λ270° U.T. 4:21 Apr 7 M.D. Y	3. 1909 Oct 4 λ270° U.T. 7:08 July 1 M.D. Y
4. 1911 Nov 26 λ275° Aug 27 M.D. Y	5. 1914 Jan 21 λ254° Oct 9 M.D. Y	6. 1916 Feb 12 λ250° U.T. 4:26 Nov 15 M.D. Y
7. 1918 Mar 31 λ284° U.T. 3:34 Dec 25 M.D. Y	8. 1920 Apr 23 λ285° U.T. 8:47 Jan 25 M.D. Y	9. 1922 June 18 λ260° U.T. 7:25 Mar 16 M.D. Y
10. 1924 Aug 31 λ250° U.T. 9:34 May 17 M.D. Y	11. 1926 Nov 6 λ255° U.T. 5:19 Aug 6 M.D. R	12. 1928 Dec 29 λ245° Sept 28 M. D. Y

Plate XIV

The large bright region between Elysium and Syrtis Major has revealed the greatest array of striking changes during the past 55 years of any part of the desert areas of Mars.

This series of yellow and red photographs, like those for the earlier years in Plate XIII, shows the varied aspects of the region preceding the Syrtis Major for different oppositions from 1931 to 1961 and displays numerous changes in the markings that have occurred there in the last thirty years. The different tilts of the planet's axis are evident, and the appearance of the northern and southern hemispheres in the different Martian seasons is indicated roughly in each case by the dimensions of the polar caps. Each opposition of the planet is represented except those of 1933, 1948 and 1950, here omitted for want of space.

Photographs Nos. 1, 2, 3, 6, 7, 8 and 12 were made near aphelion and the others were made at perihelion. The reader should make due allowance for the fact that the areas originally photographed at these positions are in the ratio of about 3.5 to 1 and that the photographs at aphelion have been enlarged to the same size as the others. However, in every case enough is recorded in the photographs to provide valid comparisons and to determine many differences in the markings and interesting changes in the various areas. In 1931 and 1935 it is evident that the Thoth-Nepenthes system of canals, as well as all the markings over the Aethiops region, was much weaker than usual. In 1937 these markings were still weak, but had been strengthened appreciably. In 1939 and 1941 these same markings had been greatly strengthened by an amount greater than can be explained by the change in the planet's distance. In October 1941 a strange and unexpected gap appeared about half way along the Thoth canal, a break which appeared complete for a distance of four or five degrees or more as if obliterated by cloud, but none was detected. Referring back to the 1939 photographs, we note that they also show the Thoth unusually weak below Lucus Moeris as compared to the other years, especially 1954 and 1956. In the red photograph, No. 9, the Thoth-Nepenthes-Triton system is by far the darkest at any time during this period and fully as prominent as it was in 1922, 1926 and 1928 (Plate XIII).

Perhaps the most extraordinary change in this region occurred around Nodus Lacoontis in 1954 just preceding the left base of the Thoth. An embryonic kernel appears to have existed there since 1952 when a small dusky patch first appeared. In 1954 this area burgeoned into a large dark area about the size of France. In most of the photographs and drawings it appeared as a fairly uniform dark shading, but when critically studied visually it was found to contain numerous details and was striated by several canals including the Eunostos, Adamas, Aethiops and Amenthes. Like the other dark areas on Mars it was not merely a uniformly shaded area but contained many lines and spots darker than itself.

Many of these developments in this region hardly belong to the ordinary seasonal type but were more irregular in character or secular in nature. In some cases the development involved the expansion of existing weak markings and in some others the development of a new dark area, not previously mapped. As is evident from the photographs, the newly developed dark markings were not of any particular type, but aside from Thoth and other areas, they were very complex in structure consisting of a maze of dark spots and striae of several kinds.

The matter of paramount importance in connection with these new dark areas, is the fact that what was once a desert region may become a dark region.

PLATE XIV

CHANGES IN THE CANALS AND DARK MARKINGS NEAR THE SYRTIS MAJOR REGION — 1931-1961.

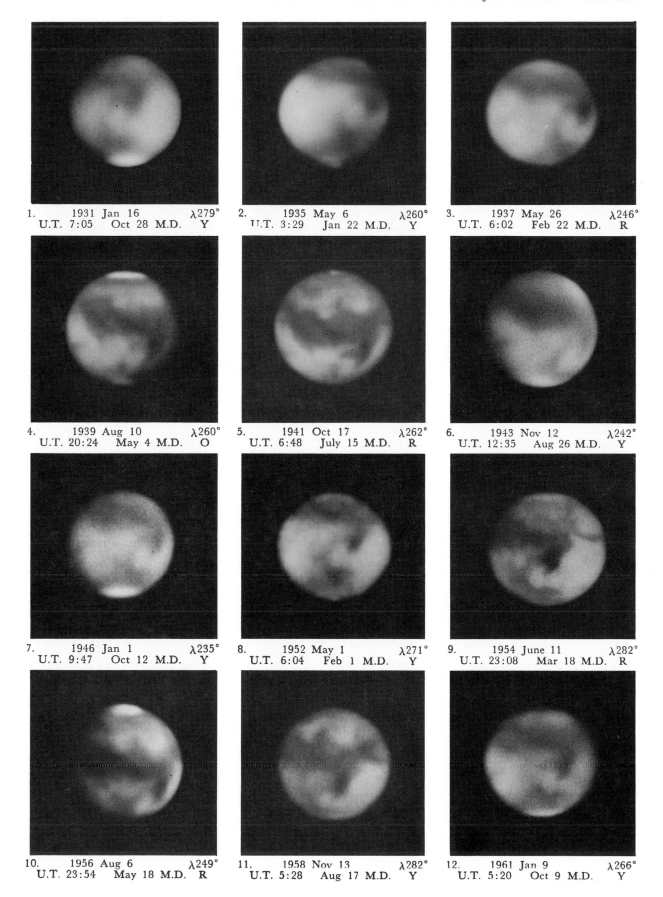

1. 1931 Jan 16 λ279° U.T. 7:05 Oct 28 M.D. Y	2. 1935 May 6 λ260° U.T. 3:29 Jan 22 M.D. Y	3. 1937 May 26 λ246° U.T. 6:02 Feb 22 M.D. R
4. 1939 Aug 10 λ260° U.T. 20:24 May 4 M.D. O	5. 1941 Oct 17 λ262° U.T. 6:48 July 15 M.D. R	6. 1943 Nov 12 λ242° U.T. 12:35 Aug 26 M.D. Y
7. 1946 Jan 1 λ235° U.T. 9:47 Oct 12 M.D. Y	8. 1952 May 1 λ271° U.T. 6:04 Feb 1 M.D. Y	9. 1954 June 11 λ282° U.T. 23:08 Mar 18 M.D. R
10. 1956 Aug 6 λ249° U.T. 23:54 May 18 M.D. R	11. 1958 Nov 13 λ282° U.T. 5:28 Aug 17 M.D. Y	12. 1961 Jan 9 λ266° U.T. 5:20 Oct 9 M.D. Y

Plate XV

Undoubtedly the outstanding revelation of the photographs is the undeniable record of seasonal darkening of vast blue-green regions in Martian summer. In 1907 we see Sabaeus Sinus standing alone in the Martian spring, but in 1909, with summer in the southern hemisphere it is seen darkly flanked by the great Pandorae Fretum in the form of a broad, dark band covering millions of square miles. Obviously if such a development occurred only once, it might be considered merely a strange coincidence. However, in 1924, with the planet again in its early spring, we note that the dark band has completely vanished into ochre desert, leaving the weak Sabaeus Sinus standing quite alone again. But in 1926 with mid-summer in the south of Mars we note that the great dark band has returned once more as a complete replica of what it was in 1909. In 1939, the dark Pandorae Fretum has disappeared again and Sabaeus Sinus stands alone, but in 1941 the summer darkening is shown returning over the Pandorae, although not to the full extent of the previous examples. In 1954, the customary winter-spring aspect is also evident. In 1956, during late Martian spring, save for a partial veiling due to haze and clouds from the widespread dust storm over most of Mars at the time, we see the customary darkening of the Pandorae Fretum region just as it has appeared in the other photographs made during summer in the south of Mars.

Although not described in connection with the foregoing series of seasonal changes, the Hellespontus, Mare Ionium, Mare Tyrrhenum also were similarily involved.

In a similar manner the series of dark regions in the southern hemisphere of the planet undergo a summer darkening. However, the Pandorae Fretum stands so completely alone on the planet that its appearance and disappearance with the Martian seasons is most obvious and the fact that it completely vanishes into the ochre desert in winter makes it by far the easiest seasonal change to recognize.

PLATE XV
SEASONAL DEVELOPMENT OF THE DARK MARKINGS
SPRING   SUMMER

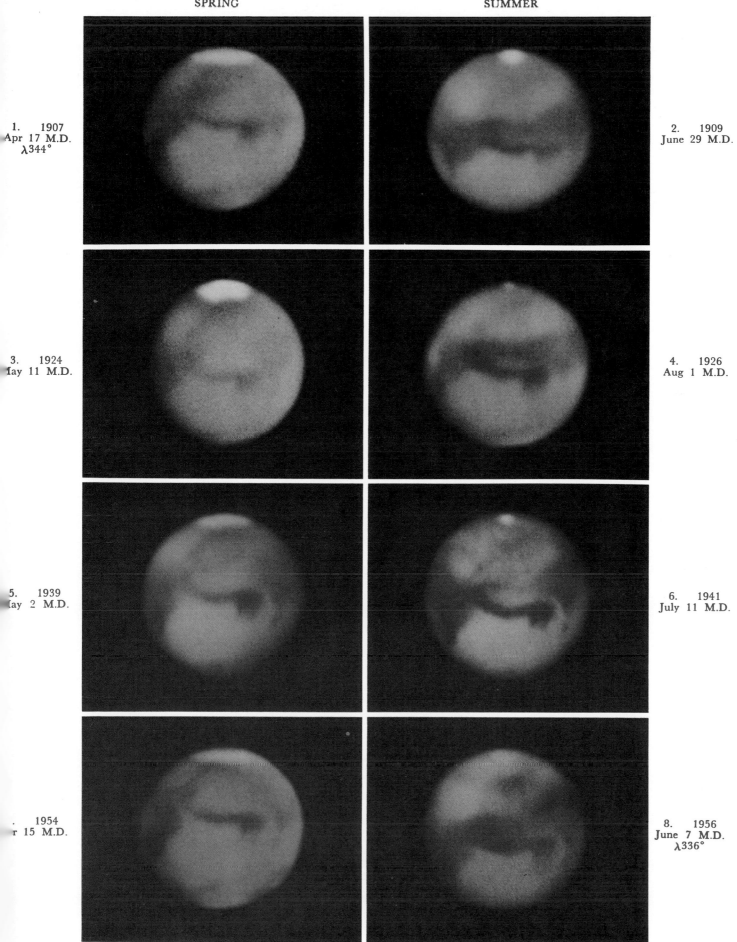

1.   1907
Apr 17 M.D.
λ344°

2.   1909
June 29 M.D.

3.   1924
May 11 M.D.

4.   1926
Aug 1 M.D.

5.   1939
May 2 M.D.

6.   1941
July 11 M.D.

1954
r 15 M.D.

8.   1956
June 7 M.D.
λ336°

Plate XVI

This series of photographs of the same face of Mars at various seasonal intervals displays stages in the progressive darkening of the blue-green regions as the cap gradually recedes towards the pole in unison with Martian spring and summer. The darkening of the maria and the southern tropics is striking from mid-May to mid-June when it appears to reach maximum intensity, and then it remains practically stationary until early September. The same general pattern of development takes place all around the planet every Martian year with remarkable regularity. In fact, at the same seasonal date the size and shape of the polar cap and other details repeat themselves with unfailing fidelity. Observers always on the lookout for departures from the systematic seasonal behavior rarely find any anomalies in the seasonal melting of the polar cap or the darkening of the dark regions. As summer advances, and the tropics darken, the polar regions and higher latitudes grow a little lighter in tone than they were in the spring.

The gradual darkening of certain regions of the planet in its summer season and their subsequent fading in winter seem best explained by attributing the dark areas to vegetation.

PLATE XVI

SEASONAL CHANGES IN THE SOUTH CAP AND DARKENING OF THE BLUE-GREEN AREAS

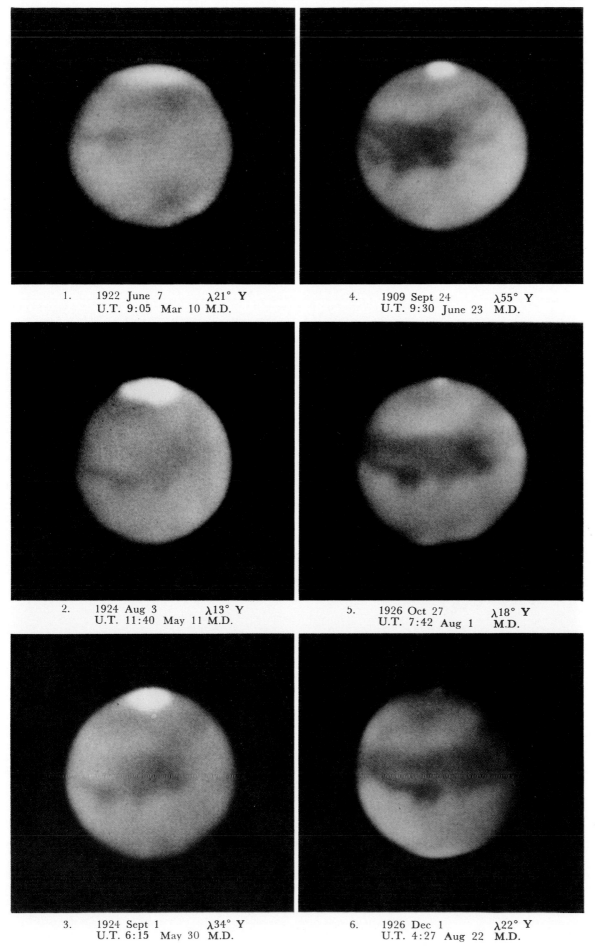

1.   1922 June 7   λ21° Y
U.T. 9:05 Mar 10 M.D.

4.   1909 Sept 24   λ55° Y
U.T. 9:30 June 23 M.D.

2.   1924 Aug 3   λ13° Y
U.T. 11:40 May 11 M.D.

5.   1926 Oct 27   λ18° Y
U.T. 7:42 Aug 1   M.D.

3.   1924 Sept 1   λ34° Y
U.T. 6:15 May 30 M.D.

6.   1926 Dec 1   λ22° Y
U.T. 4:27 Aug 22 M.D.

Plate XVII

The first 8 photographs illustrate further the various shapes and sizes the cap undergoes every Martian spring and summer in its retreat to the pole and the orderly precision with which it recedes with the advance of summer.

It has long been observed that as the snow cap melts it is always outlined by a dark collar which hugs the cap as it recedes. In order to show that this dark band is not merely a contrast effect, we have added a series of photographs from 1918 to 1952 showing the north cap in mid-summer. Contrast obviously plays no part in the appearance of the dark band, because in the red pictures the snow is no brighter than the surrounding desert. The dark band common to both caps in season has always been explained as being caused by moisture released by the melting cap. Thus the photographs fully confirm what has been known from visual observation, although contested by some, for half a century.

PLATE XVII
SEASONAL MELTING OF THE SOUTH POLAR CAP AND THE APPEARANCE OF THE DARK COLLAR.

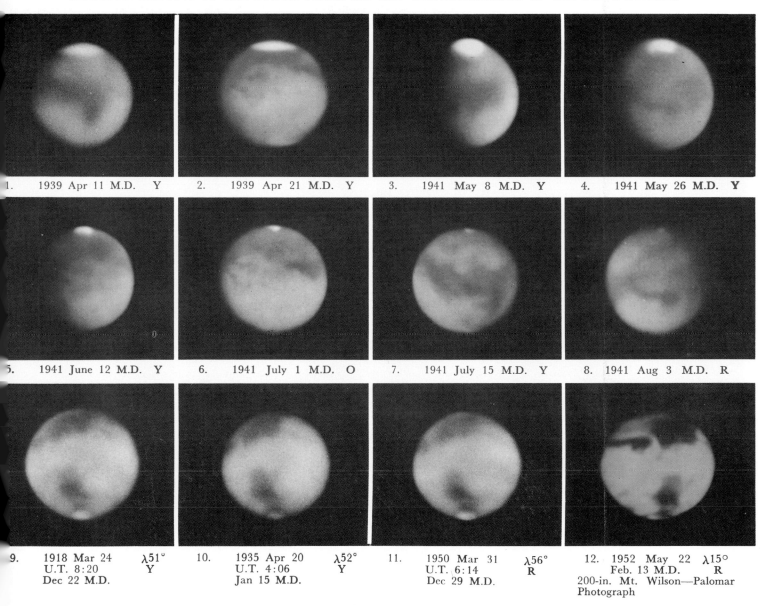

1. 1939 Apr 11 M.D. Y   2. 1939 Apr 21 M.D. Y   3. 1941 May 8 M.D. Y   4. 1941 May 26 M.D. Y

5. 1941 June 12 M.D. Y   6. 1941 July 1 M.D. O   7. 1941 July 15 M.D. Y   8. 1941 Aug 3 M.D. R

9. 1918 Mar 24 λ51°   10. 1935 Apr 20 λ52°   11. 1950 Mar 31 λ56°   12. 1952 May 22 λ15°
U.T. 8:20 Y   U.T. 4:06 Y   U.T. 6:14 R   Feb. 13 M.D. R
Dec 22 M.D.   Jan 15 M.D.   Dec 29 M.D.   200-in. Mt. Wilson—Palomar
Photograph

Plate XVIII

Since 1907 when photographic observations of Mars became a regular part of our observational program, the behavior of the polar caps has proved to be one of pertinent significance. These representative yellow photographs clearly portray the persistent character of the south snow cap in Martian springtime as it slowly shrinks toward the pole. At the same time they reveal sudden changes in the north cap in autumn when that cap consists of clouds of intermittent character. One can see in Nos. 1, 2 and 3, taken on July 15, 16 and 17 in 1907, the stability of the waning south snow cap. During the same period the waxing north cap formed of cloud, was large on the first night, had all but disappeared on the second, but on the third had returned again to much the same size as on the first. The marked difference in the brightness and behavior in the two caps strongly indicates that the brighter one was a bright substance, such as snow, ice or frost deposited on the surface, which only gradually changes with the season. The duller one, however, at the autumn pole formed and dissipated from night to night and denoted clouds in the atmosphere.

Photographs 4, 5 and 6, in 1939, show the notably different character of the two polar caps—a solid deposit on the surface in the one case, and atmospheric clouds in the other. Nos. 7, 8 and 9 taken on successive nights and showing the same face of the planet, reveal a repetition of the behavior of the two types of polar caps. The same may be said of the last three prints. The Lowell collection of photographs of Mars over a period of 58 years portrays this same performance of the summer and winter caps many times.

Martian dates given on this plate, except for the top row, have been computed for the planet's northern hemisphere rather than for the southern hemisphere, which is customarily used.

36

PLATE XVIII

PERSISTENCE OF SOLID SOUTH CAP IN SPRINGTIME AND RAPID CHANGES IN CLOUD CANOPY AT AUTUMN POLE.

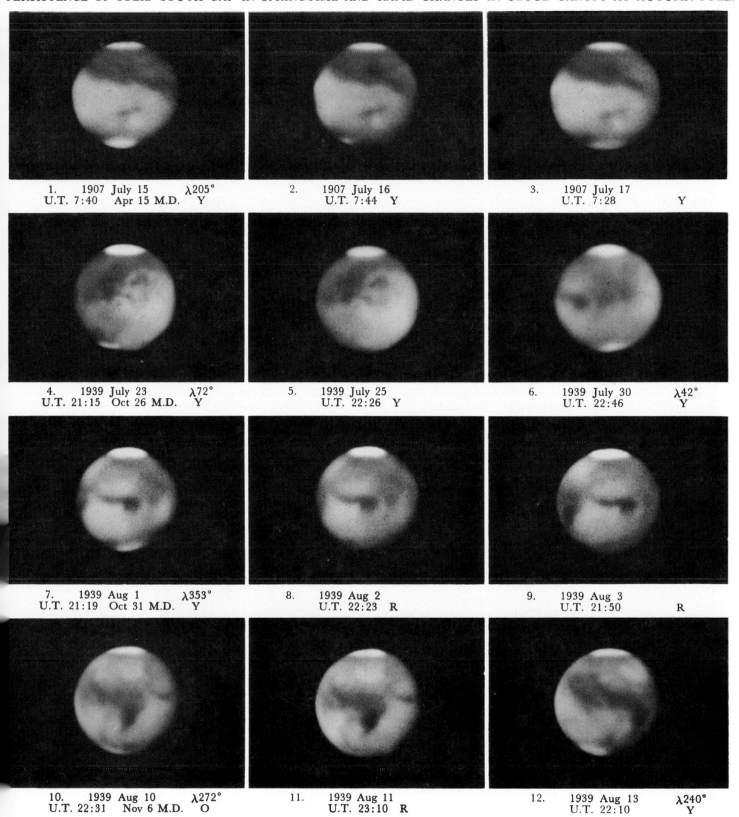

1.   1907 July 15   λ205°
U.T. 7:40 Apr 15 M.D. Y

2.   1907 July 16
U.T. 7:44 Y

3.   1907 July 17
U.T. 7:28   Y

4.   1939 July 23   λ72°
U.T. 21:15 Oct 26 M.D. Y

5.   1939 July 25
U.T. 22:26 Y

6.   1939 July 30   λ42°
U.T. 22:46   Y

7.   1939 Aug 1   λ353°
U.T. 21:19 Oct 31 M.D. Y

8.   1939 Aug 2
U.T. 22:23 R

9.   1939 Aug 3
U.T. 21:50   R

10.   1939 Aug 10   λ272°
U.T. 22:31 Nov 6 M.D. O

11.   1939 Aug 11
U.T. 23:10 R

12.   1939 Aug 13   λ240°
U.T. 22:10   Y

Plate XIX

These monochromatic photographs are intended to show a fundamental fact concerning the snow caps revealed by blue light. The six photographs selected here for comparison represent Mars under various atmospheric conditions: No. 1, completely opaque; No. 3, virtually transparent; No. 5, semi-transparent.

Since 1909, Lowell Observatory photographs taken in blue and violet light have strongly recorded the snow cap even when the planet's atmosphere was so opaque to the blue rays as to totally obscure all the other surface features. Later observers who obtained the same results were puzzled at this seeming paradox and therefore postulated a high cloud canopy over the cap to explain its appearance in the blue photographs. It had long been known that the polar caps are sometimes seen divided and broken by rifts or bright and dark patches. They often show irregular outlines and divisions which have been observed to occur repeatedly at the same places and at the same seasons.

Since 1922, observations at Flagstaff with blue filters have revealed these details in blue light, but convincing photographs of them have been very difficult to obtain. Blue photographs, however, have always shown the shape, size and contour of the cap to be the same as they appeared in yellow pictures made at the same time. This is illustrated by comparing Nos. 3 and 4, and 5 and 6. It was also found that this close resemblance was maintained from spring to late summer with a constancy hardly to be expected of a cloud cap. This was especially so in view of the spectacular variations continually occurring in the cloud cap at the opposite pole which sometimes covered several millions of square miles on one night and had vanished completely on the next. Finally near the end of August 1956, under favorable circumstances for such observations, the cap was caught undergoing rapid disintegration near the time of opposition. The blue pictures revealed the same broken, divided character of the cap as that shown by images Nos. 1 and 2. This had often been seen visually. The results clearly and definitely proved that the blue cap was in fact the same object as that observed in red and yellow light—an actual deposit on the planet's surface. A comparison of Nos. 1 and 2 discloses that the left-hand one-third of the cap is fainter, broken, and more irregular than the larger, brighter, right-hand portion. A dark rift, too fine to show clearly in the composite photographs, divides the two sections.

Hundreds of photographs taken at Bloemfontein support these facts. All of the other surface features in blue light (No. 1) were completely obscured in August, 1956, so the planet's atmosphere was quite opaque but the cap appeared similar in blue and red light.

38

PLATE XIX
PHOTOGRAPHS OF SOUTH CAP IN BLUE LIGHT COMPARED WITH THOSE MADE IN RED, ORANGE AND YELLOW.

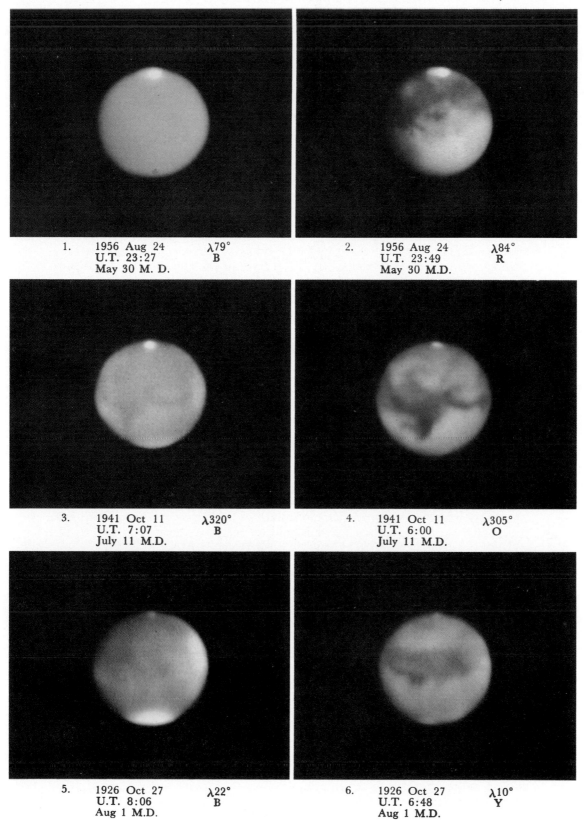

1. 1956 Aug 24   λ79°
    U.T. 23:27   B
    May 30 M. D.

2. 1956 Aug 24   λ84°
    U.T. 23:49   R
    May 30 M.D.

3. 1941 Oct 11   λ320°
    U.T. 7:07   B
    July 11 M.D.

4. 1941 Oct 11   λ305°
    U.T. 6:00   O
    July 11 M.D.

5. 1926 Oct 27   λ22°
    U.T. 8:06   B
    Aug 1 M.D.

6. 1926 Oct 27   λ10°
    U.T. 6:48   Y
    Aug 1 M.D.

Plate XX

These photographs display three stages in the seasonal behavior of the south cap. No. 1 (yellow) shows the winter cloud cap on March 6 (Martian Date) extending down nearly to the Solis Lacus (dark spot upper right). This extension, nearly 100° in breadth, means that if the polar canopy were symmetrical, its maximum diameter (measured along the surface) exceeded 3,500 miles. However, in this instance, as is generally the case in winter, the cloud cap far exceeds the actual size of the ice cap when it later is exposed to our view after the vernal equinox. After the longer, colder winter in the south of Mars, the snow cap there reaches 73° in breadth, while the shorter, warmer winter in the northern hemisphere produces a snow cap scarcely more than 53° across. More than a century of observations show that the caps at the two poles always maintain this same angular ratio. On the other hand, the short, hot summers in the southern hemisphere always melt the southern cap to a smaller compass, sometimes completely melting it away (1894 and 1908). The longer, cooler summers in the northern hemisphere never reduce its cap to a smaller compass than 5°.

No. 2 is a yellow photograph portraying the south cap on Martian August 17 when it is nearing its minimum size (compare edge of cap with Solis Lacus in No. 1) and measures scarcely 100 miles across.

No. 3 is a blue photograph showing the planet near its equinoxes; the southern hemisphere is just past its autumnal equinox, while the northern one is just passing the vernal equinox. Here the cloud canopies over both poles reach down the disk to latitudes below 40°.

Monochromatic photographs of the same face of Mars made in red (4), orange (5), yellow (6), and blue (7) demonstrate the redness of the disk and the blueness of its snow cap. In No. 4 the albedo of the snow in red light (6200-6700A) is so low as compared to the disk that the cap appears scarcely as bright as the desert areas. In orange light (5600-6200A), the brightness of the cap rises slightly above that of the desert regions. In the yellow-green (5000-5700A), the snow cap greatly exceeds the rest of the disk in brightness, while in violet light (3900-4600A), the snow cap far outshines anything on the disk and is rivaled only by the cloud canopy over the north polar region.

These images from four regions of the spectrum show the high color-index of Mars, the bluish tint of the snow cap, and readily explain why the spectrum of the disk reveals a low albedo toward the shorter wavelengths as is shown by all spectrographic observations. On the other hand, the snow cap is so brilliant in blue and ultraviolet light that absorption by the Martian atmosphere registers no appreciable effect. Obviously here the snow cap is observed through the equivalent of many atmospheres yet it progressively brightens toward the shorter wavelengths.

This brightening is of major importance. It argues strongly against the new theory[1] that nitrogen dioxide and nitrogen tetroxide explain the clouds, polar caps and the changes in the dark markings. It appears that the sole evidence for the new theory rests on the assumption that the weakness of the spectrum of the disk of the planet toward the violet is due to absorption of nitrogen dioxide; on the contrary, these observations show that this weakening must be due to selective reflection from the red disk of Mars.

---

[1]Kiess, C. C., Karrer, S. and Kiess, H. K., 1960, P.A.S.P., 72, 427, p. 256.

PLATE XX

EXTREMES IN THE AREA OF SOUTH POLAR CAP.

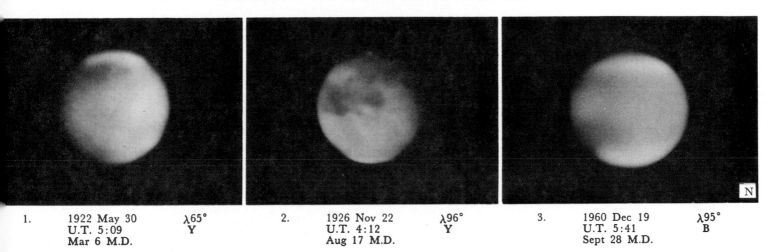

| 1. | 1922 May 30
U.T. 5:09
Mar 6 M.D. | λ65°
Y | 2. | 1926 Nov 22
U.T. 4:12
Aug 17 M.D. | λ96°
Y | 3. | 1960 Dec 19
U.T. 5:41
Sept 28 M.D. | λ95°
B |

RELATIVE BRIGHTNESS OF POLAR CAPS IN 4-COLORS

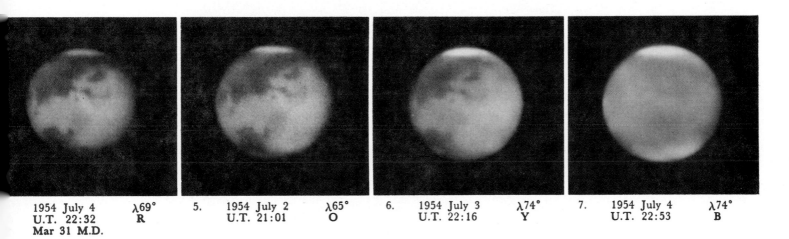

| | 1954 July 4
U.T. 22:32
Mar 31 M.D. | λ69°
R | 5. | 1954 July 2
U.T. 21:01 | λ65°
O | 6. | 1954 July 3
U.T. 22:16 | λ74°
Y | 7. | 1954 July 4
U.T. 22:53 | λ74°
B |

Plate XXI

The adjoining photographs display one of the most revealing events in the retreat of the south cap to the pole. I refer to the small bright spot to the left of the main cap, a detached patch of snow which is left behind as the dwindling cap recedes toward the pole during summer. Circumstances of Martian seasons and occurrence of opposition are such that this event can only be observed at intervals of about 15 years. First observed by Mitchel at Cincinnati in 1845, it has occurred with remarkable coincidence on practically the same seasonal date at every opposition.

The following table shows all the available observations since its discovery.

OBSERVATIONS OF THE MTS. OF MITCHEL

Observer	Date	Corresponding Martian Date
Mitchel	Aug. 30, 1845	May 31
Green	Sep. 1, 1877	June 3
Brett	Sep. 1, 1877	June 3
Lowell	Aug. 6, 1894	June 4
W. W. Campbell	Aug. 7, 1894	June 4.5
Barnard	Aug. 6, 1894	June 4
W. H. Pickering	Aug. 6, 1894	June 4
Douglass	Aug. 8, 1894	June 5
E. C. Slipher	Aug. 21, 1909 Photo	June 2
E. C. Slipher	Sep. 7, 1924 Photo	June 3
Trumpler	Sep. 7, 1924	June 3
E. C. Slipher	Aug 1, 1941 Photo	May 31
E. C. Slipher	Aug. 31, 1956 Photo	June 3

The slight discrepancy in the seasonal dates of the 1845 and the 1941 observations, as compared to the others, is noticeable because these were made at an earlier stage in the development of the spot. During my observations of 1941 the patch had not reduced to the same degree as at the oppositions cited in the table, and it was not possible to observe the planet at this stage before it was lost in the daylight sky.

Besides the interest in this remarkable event itself, the importance lies in the precise mile post it provides in the systematic retreat of the south cap, arriving on practically the same Martian date year after year.

Another phenomenon connected with the site of this snow patch is that on several occasions, as for example in November, 1909, and in October, 1941, approximately three months after the snow on the Mts. of Mitchel had disappeared, a patch of temporary mist or cloud of the same size and shape appeared over the same area. (See No. 6, Plate XV.)

PLATE XXI

FOUR OCCURRENCES OF THE MOUNTAINS OF MITCHEL FROM 1909 TO 1956.

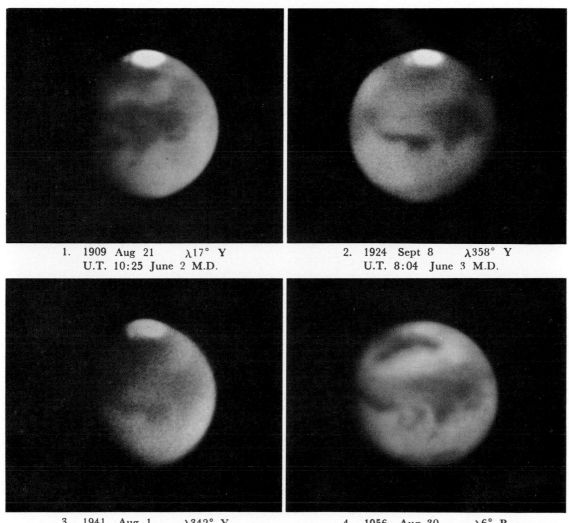

1. 1909 Aug 21   λ17° Y
   U.T. 10:25 June 2 M.D.

2. 1924 Sept 8   λ358° Y
   U.T. 8:04 June 3 M.D.

3. 1941 Aug 1   λ342° Y
   U.T. 13:38 May 27 M.D.

4. 1956 Aug 30   λ6° R
   U.T. 22:05 June 3 M.D.

Plate XXII

These observations are arranged to display the life history of a remarkable storm over the Martian tropics (bright area near center of disk), embracing about 400,000 square miles. It appeared first on July 9, 1922, as a nearly rectangular-shaped bright spot. It stood out brilliantly at the first look at the planet where nothing unusual had been observed on the night before. Photographs on the first night revealed that the cloud was nearly as bright in the yellow as was the polar cap. Blue photographs made at the same time with the 42-inch reflector by Lampland (CL, No. 5) showed it to be no brighter than the rest of the disk. This indicated a strong yellowish tint of the cloud, which by selective reflection reduced its albedo in blue to that of the general background of the blue photograph (note here how much larger and brighter the polar caps appear in the blue image because of their strong blue color).

On July 10 the cloud area had moved appreciably towards the northwest and had also expanded very considerably in that direction, showing a thinning and flaring out over the desert area to the north. Photographs on the 11th (not included here) revealed further expansion and disintegration into small spots over a considerable area with the whole storm still moving slowly to the northwest. It was not then possible to identify with certainty the original cloud center. On July 12, the cloud area had so generally dissipated and scattered that it showed only as a thin, faint veil obscuring the coast line and desert northeast of the base of Margaritifer Sinus. This storm lasted for four days, the longest period of any the writer had observed until that time.

The motion of this storm was abnormally slow—6 to 12 miles per hour. The precise value would depend upon what expansion factor is applied. On the first night, before expansion was observed, it was barely possible to detect motion, estimated at 6 miles per hour. But on the second night, July 10, the expansion and the drift of the cloud area are clear and distinct in the photographs. Unfortunately this outstanding storm was not observed anywhere else in the world, so our knowledge of its life history is confined to the Flagstaff observations.[1]

---

[1]Slipher, E. C., 1922, P.A.S.P., *34*, 22.

PLATE XXII

THE GREAT STORM OF 1922

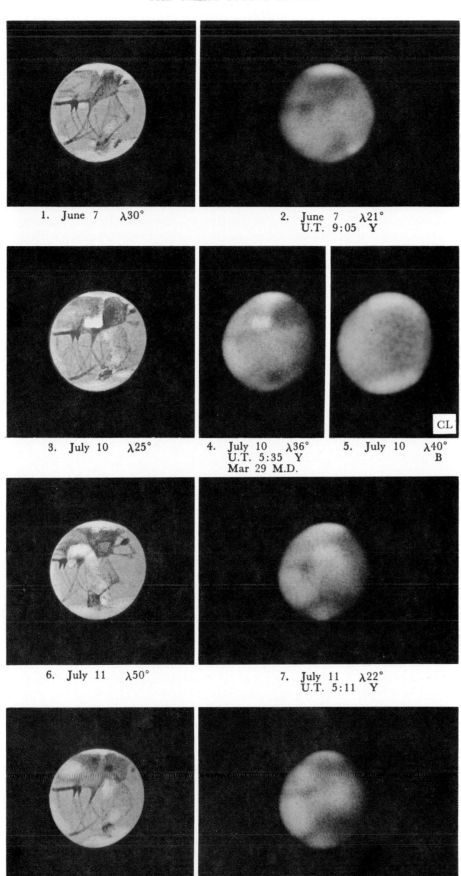

1. June 7   λ30°

2. June 7   λ21°
   U.T. 9:05 Y

3. July 10   λ25°

4. July 10   λ36°
   U.T. 5:35 Y
   Mar 29 M.D.

5. July 10   λ40°
   B

CL

6. July 11   λ50°

7. July 11   λ22°
   U.T. 5:11 Y

8. July 13   λ25°

9. July 13   λ23°
   U.T. 6:26 Y

Plate XXIII

Shown here is a photographic history of one of the most remarkable meteorological phenomena ever observed on.Mars. It was first observed visually and photographed by the writer at the opposition in 1907. A similar cloud group has been repeatedly observed in the same locale, the Tharsis region near Lacus Phoenicis. During later oppositions, as for example in October, 1926, and June, 1954, the configuration received the designation "the W clouds". Similar blue photographs of the same face of the planet in 1956, made in late Martian May and early June, failed to show the brilliant cloud group present in 1954.

The most remarkable peculiarity of these clouds is that they are strictly an afternoon event. They appear faintly first around two o'clock and gradually develop and brighten during the afternoon until, toward the sunset limb, they become so prominent and bright as to rival the snow cap in brilliance. On the next morning, they are entirely gone, only to reappear in the early afternoon and gradually repeat themselves in the same place and in the exact same pattern during the afternoon. Sometimes, as in 1954, this cloud group repeats itself each afternoon for a period of three weeks or more. The configuration appears the same each day and no shift in the cloud masses has been observed; the whole pattern rotating with the planet.

Another remarkable feature of this phenomenon is that the main stems of the cloud pattern appear to coincide with the main canals in the area.

A marked tendency for clouds to recur for several decades over one part of the planet's surface has been observed since 1907. One such area lies near Phoenicis Lacus and particularly on its following side, as well as above and below it. The writer has observed temporary clouds in this vicinity many times in the past half century and while he has not made an exhaustive search of the files to form a complete list, a partial list shows examples in 1907, 1909, 1920, 1924, 1926, 1935, 1954, 1956 and 1958. On August 18, 1941, (M.D. = June 6) Truman photographed at Mt. Wilson a 350-mile cloud near Phoenicis Lacus (latitude $-17°$ and longitude $116°$) which is the approximate location of one of the strong clouds in the "W" group of 1954. The prevalence of recurrent clouds in this general area suggests that they may owe their origin to some geographical conditions or physical process associated with this location on the planet's surface. McLaughlin (1954) believes that the explanation may lie in his hypothesis of volcanic activity there.[1] However, the temporary and even seasonal character of these clouds obviously militate against the volcanic origin idea.

In addition to being the site of this interesting array of brilliant white clouds, this same area has at other times, namely August 1939 and September 1956, become the scene of very abnormal darkening of the markings; the darkening being far greater than any other change in the surrounding desert. As near as can be determined the darkest spots and markings then occupied the same places as did the brightest parts of the cloud pattern. While the clouds appeared only in the Martian afternoon, the dark markings referred to here always appeared to me to be somewhat darker and more conspicuous in the Martian forenoons. If moisture released by the melting snow caps causes the summer darkening of other regions on Mars, it seems reasonable to conclude that moisture released by these clouds may have caused the unusual darkening of these markings.[2]

[1]McLaughlin, D. B., 1954, Sky and Tel., *13*, No. 11, p. 372.
[2]Slipher, E. C., 1962, *The Photographic Story of Mars,* Plate XLV.

PLATE XXIII

SERIES SHOWING W-SHAPED CLOUD BELOW LACUS PHOENICIS

1954

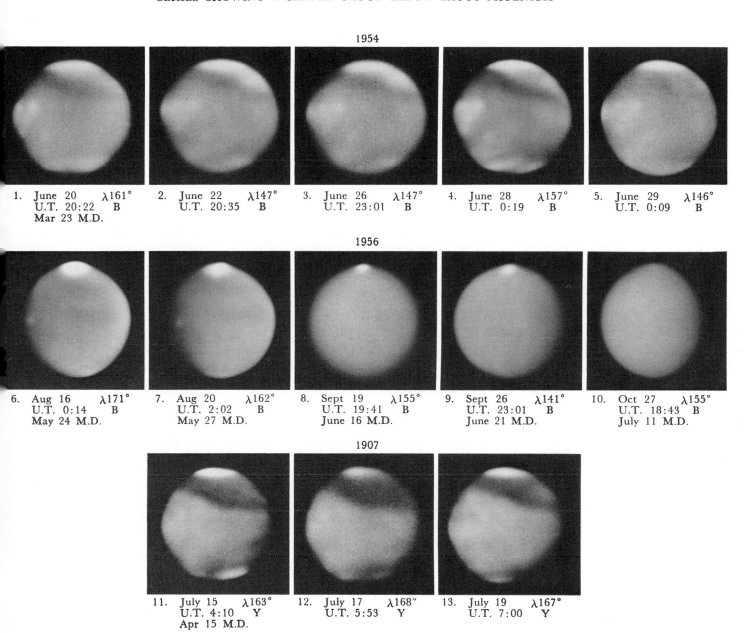

1. June 20   λ161°
    U.T. 20:22   B
    Mar 23 M.D.

2. June 22   λ147°
    U.T. 20:35   B

3. June 26   λ147°
    U.T. 23:01   B

4. June 28   λ157°
    U.T. 0:19   B

5. June 29   λ146°
    U.T. 0:09   B

1956

6. Aug 16   λ171°
    U.T. 0:14   B
    May 24 M.D.

7. Aug 20   λ162°
    U.T. 2:02   B
    May 27 M.D.

8. Sept 19   λ155°
    U.T. 19:41   B
    June 16 M.D.

9. Sept 26   λ141°
    U.T. 23:01   B
    June 21 M.D.

10. Oct 27   λ155°
    U.T. 18:43   B
    July 11 M.D.

1907

11. July 15   λ163°
    U.T. 4:10   Y
    Apr 15 M.D.

12. July 17   λ168°
    U.T. 5:53   Y

13. July 19   λ167°
    U.T. 7:00   Y

Plate XXIV

On the whole disk of Mars, no region is so frequently invaded by yellow clouds as the Libya and Isidis regions on the preceding side of the Syrtis Major. The photographs illustrate the behavior of three separate examples of temporary cloud areas in this region in the 1924, 1943 and 1958 apparitions.

In 1920 the clouds were observed on three successive nights and the cloud area was sufficiently well defined to show not only the direction of its motion but the rate of motion as well. If we exclude the expansion factor, which usually becomes quite large after a period of about 48 hours, in all three examples the motion was southeasterly at a rate of 20 to 30 miles per hour.

In 1924 (upper row) the cloud area appeared first as a small spot near the edge of the Syrtis Major and was seen to be moving southward; on the following night it was situated just south of the Thoth over the Libya. Since it showed no appreciable expansion, its rate of motion of 22 miles per hour is probably a good determination of the wind velocity.

In 1943 a cloud area was first observed in the Libya region (see second row), moved mostly eastward and expanded considerably on the second night, while on the third night its expansion and motion had carried it southwesterly over the southern portion of the Hesperia strait.

In 1958 a cloud appeared first in the Isidis region on October 13th and moved into the northern Libya on the 14th. On the 15th it had expanded considerably; this expansion and its motion, had carried it mostly eastward. On the 16th its further expansion and motion had carried the forward portion over the southern part of the Hesperia. Thus the motion of these clouds, allowing for expansion, turned out to be from 22 to 30 miles per hour in a southeasterly direction.

48

PLATE XXIV

SERIES SHOWING YELLOW CLOUDS IN ISIDIS AND LIBYA REGIONS, 1924 — 1943 — 1958.

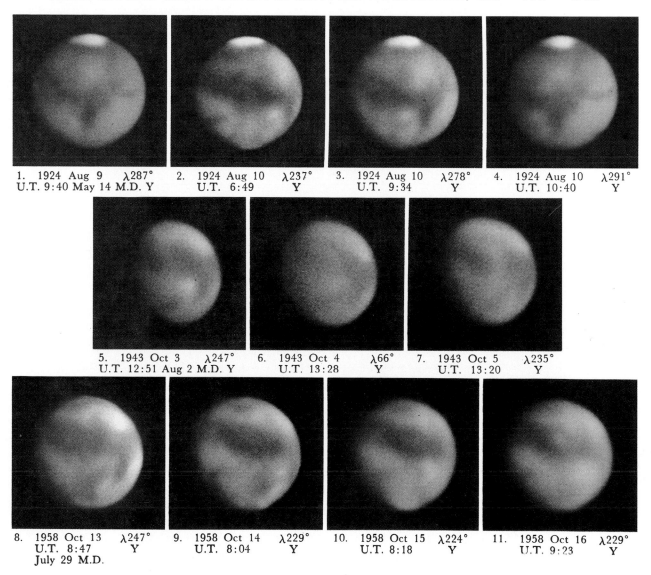

1. 1924 Aug 9   λ287°
U.T. 9:40 May 14 M.D. Y

2. 1924 Aug 10   λ237°
U.T. 6:49   Y

3. 1924 Aug 10   λ278°
U.T. 9:34   Y

4. 1924 Aug 10   λ291°
U.T. 10:40   Y

5. 1943 Oct 3   λ247°
U.T. 12:51 Aug 2 M.D. Y

6. 1943 Oct 4   λ66°
U.T. 13:28   Y

7. 1943 Oct 5   λ235°
U.T. 13:20   Y

8. 1958 Oct 13   λ247°
U.T. 8:47   Y
July 29 M.D.

9. 1958 Oct 14   λ229°
U.T. 8:04   Y

10. 1958 Oct 15 λ224°
U.T. 8:18   Y

11. 1958 Oct 16 λ229°
U.T. 9:23   Y

Plate XXV

Photographs made in red or yellow light in 1956 are compared with those obtained in 1941 when the Martian atmosphere was normally clear. The missing dark markings in the 1956 photographs result from the obscuration by atmospheric clouds. In some instances there is only a general weakening of the dark areas, but in other cases, (as in No. 2), they are completely concealed or broken up into irregular patches. It will be noted in Nos. 1, 2, 3 and 7, that the south snow cap is all but hidden from view by the heavy cloud cover. In Nos. 8 and 9 the obscuring veil over the cap has become more tenuous and the cap itself begins to approach its normal appearance. (In Nos. 7, 8, 9, G=Giclas.)

Accompanying the storm clouds there were numerous cases of abnormal darkening of certain areas, as for example near Aurora Sinus and the dark spot to the left of the Solis Lacus as in No. 8.

In general there were more cloud areas in the southern hemisphere; but in photographs 2, 3 and 9 the clouds invaded the northern hemisphere and concealed familiar markings there. The density, expanse, and duration of this storm was undoubtedly the greatest ever observed during the recorded history of the planet.

PLATE XXV
PHOTOGRAPHS DURING DUST STORM 1956 AND COMPARATIVE 1941 NORMAL SERIES

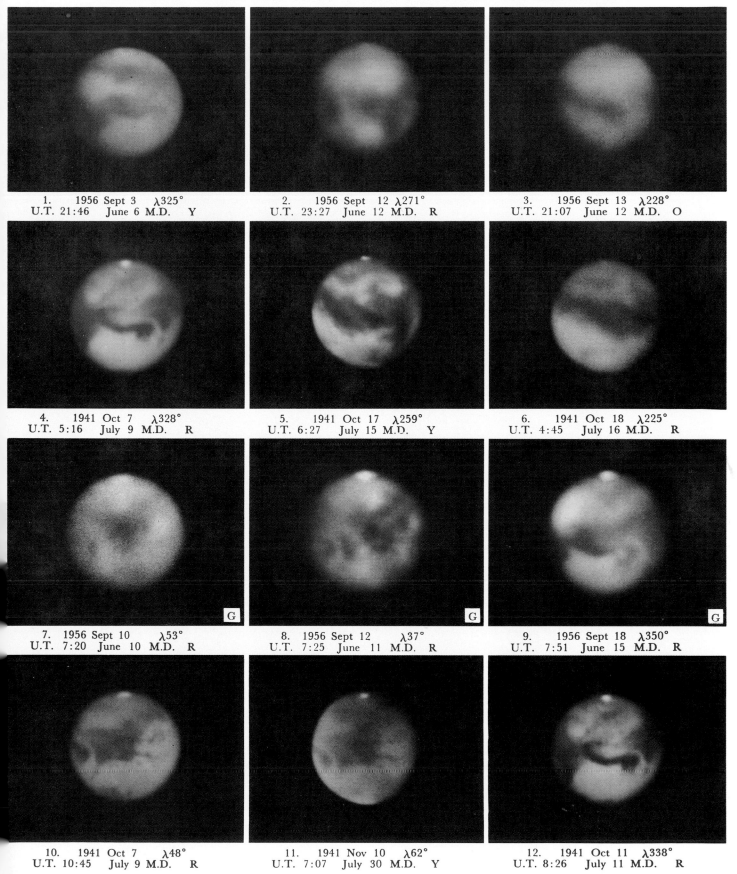

1. 1956 Sept 3 λ325° U.T. 21:46 June 6 M.D. Y	2. 1956 Sept 12 λ271° U.T. 23:27 June 12 M.D. R	3. 1956 Sept 13 λ228° U.T. 21:07 June 12 M.D. O
4. 1941 Oct 7 λ328° U.T. 5:16 July 9 M.D. R	5. 1941 Oct 17 λ259° U.T. 6:27 July 15 M.D. Y	6. 1941 Oct 18 λ225° U.T. 4:45 July 16 M.D. R
7. 1956 Sept 10 λ53° U.T. 7:20 June 10 M.D. R	8. 1956 Sept 12 λ37° U.T. 7:25 June 11 M.D. R	9. 1956 Sept 18 λ350° U.T. 7:51 June 15 M.D. R
10. 1941 Oct 7 λ48° U.T. 10:45 July 9 M.D. R	11. 1941 Nov 10 λ62° U.T. 7:07 July 30 M.D. Y	12. 1941 Oct 11 λ338° U.T. 8:26 July 11 M.D. R

Plate XXVI

During the past 34 years the Martian atmosphere, usually opaque in blue light, has often cleared suddenly so that for three or four days the surface features are remarkably distinct. Several times between 1926 and 1958 periods of transparency coincided quite closely with opposition. These blue images (only two or three for each occasion) illustrate the more remarkable examples of outstanding blue clearing. Nos. 1, 2 and 3 show the region from Syrtis Major to Meridiani Sinus, with Pandorae Fretum above, as revealed from November 1 to 5, 1926.[1,2] Familiar dark markings are almost as prominent as in a mediocre yellow photograph. Allowing for selective reflection in reducing the contrast between dark areas and deserts in blue light as shown in Plate XII, we conclude that the atmosphere was almost completely transparent to blue light. Since blue clearing seems more prevalent near opposition, it is noteworthy that this outstanding blue clearing exactly coincided with the planet's opposition on Nov. 4.

Nos. 4 and 5 show unusual blue clearing on December 29, 1928, eight days after opposition. Nos. 6 and 7, taken two and three days respectively after the 1937 opposition, show Syrtis Major remarkably clear except for patches of misty bluish clouds. Blue photographs compare favorably with yellow photographs made at the same time in showing surface markings.

At the next opposition in 1941, Nos. 8, 10 and 11 show extraordinary blue clearing on October 9, 10 and 11. Again this example of blue clearing, like those in 1926 and 1937, was centered precisely with the opposition date of October 10. On this occasion the blue clearing was estimated as 4 to 5 on a scale 0-5 with 5 perfectly clear. On June 14, 1954, No. 12 shows another example of maximum blue clearing where the Syrtis Major and Mare Tyrrhenum are so clearly recorded as to rival the best yellow photographs. This occurred ten days before opposition. No. 13, taken within one day of opposition, shows the atmosphere completely opaque again and it remained essentially so for the remainder of the apparition. During the earlier part of the 1954 opposition there were numerous instances of strong or partial blue clearing during the Martian late winter.

In the first half of the opposition of 1956 the blue photographs showed that the atmosphere was continually opaque up to the advent of the great dust storm near the end of August. Nos. 14 and 15, however, show blue photographs taken on September 1 and 3, respectively, which reveal an abnormal amount of blue clearing although they were made at the very height of the greatest dust storm ever recorded on the planet. Although the photographs are heavily mottled by patches of dense clouds, enough of the Syrtis Major, Sabaeus Sinus, Pandorae Fretum, Hellespontus and Mare Australe are revealed between clouds to show that better-than-average blue clearing was present. The fact that blue clearing could occur during the height of such an enormous dust storm clearly demonstrates that dust is not the medium which produces the violet layer as some authors have theoretically concluded. In 1958 blue photographs on November 13 and 14 (Nos. 16 and 17) show the best blue clearing during the whole apparition. This again occurred within four days of opposition on November 17.

[1]Slipher, E. C., 1927, P.A.S.P., *39,* No. 230.
[2]——————, 1938, Proc. Amer. Phil. Soc., *79,* No. 3.

PLATE XXVI
CHARACTERISTIC BLUE CLEARING NEAR OPPOSITIONS FROM 1926 TO 1958.

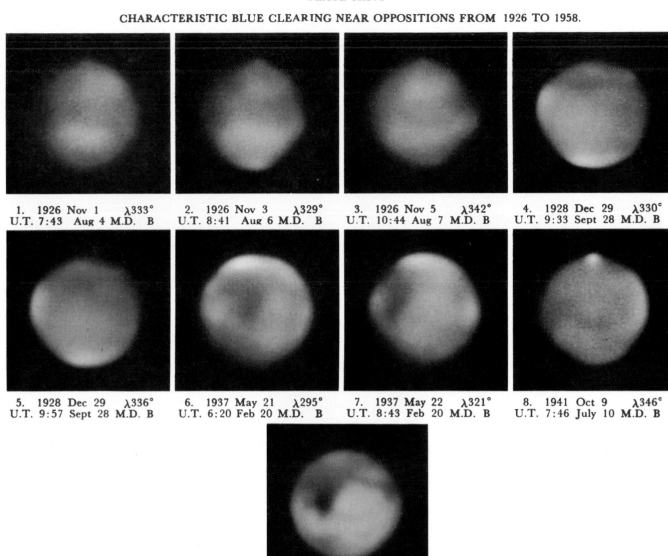

1. 1926 Nov 1   λ333°
U.T. 7:43   Aug 4 M.D. B

2. 1926 Nov 3   λ329°
U.T. 8:41   Aug 6 M.D. B

3. 1926 Nov 5   λ342°
U.T. 10:44 Aug 7 M.D. B

4. 1928 Dec 29   λ330°
U.T. 9:33   Sept 28 M.D. B

5. 1928 Dec 29   λ336°
U.T. 9:57   Sept 28 M.D. B

6. 1937 May 21   λ295°
U.T. 6:20   Feb 20 M.D. B

7. 1937 May 22   λ321°
U.T. 8:43   Feb 20 M.D. B

8. 1941 Oct 9   λ346°
U.T. 7:46   July 10 M.D. B

9. 1937 May 21   λ305°
U.T. 7:41   Feb 20 M.D. Y

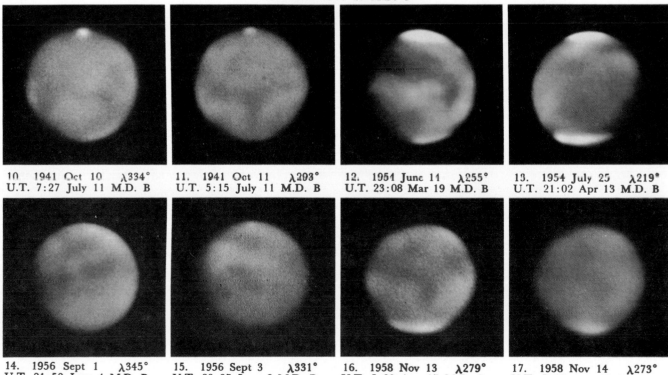

10. 1941 Oct 10   λ334°
U.T. 7:27   July 11 M.D. B

11. 1941 Oct 11   λ293°
U.T. 5:15   July 11 M.D. B

12. 1954 June 11   λ255°
U.T. 23:08 Mar 19 M.D. B

13. 1954 July 25   λ219°
U.T. 21:02 Apr 13 M.D. B

14. 1956 Sept 1   λ345°
U.T. 21:52 June 4 M.D. B

15. 1956 Sept 3   λ331°
U.T. 22:07 June 6 M.D. B

16. 1958 Nov 13   λ279°
U.T. 5:08   Aug 17 M.D. B

17. 1958 Nov 14   λ273°
U.T. 5:18   Aug 17 M.D. B

Plate XXVII

If we compare blue photographs taken far from opposition with corresponding yellow or red examples of the identical face of Mars (Plates IX and X), it appears that they occasionally show a fairly high degree of blue clearing and much of the maria are visible. In some cases the atmospheric transparency was estimated to be three to four. Such extraordinary blue clearing, so far from opposition, came as a surprise because all the early examples of unusual blue clearing had occurred at opposition time, namely 1926, 1928, 1937 and 1941. This seemingly well-established relation between blue clearing and opposition date led to attempts to explain the phenomena on the basis of circumstances existing only at the time of opposition. Such examples as these, however, and similar ones observed here and elsewhere, strongly indicate that circumstances existing at opposition are not necessarily a prerequisite to blue clearing.

Naturally at opposition when the Sun and Earth are in line with Mars, the incident and reflected light transverse the minimum possible atmospheric path, a condition which is conducive to a clearer view of the surface. If the surface of the planet had been observed through the minimum path it seems probable that these photographs might have been so enhanced as to rival the remarkable examples of blue clearing observed at the oppositions of 1937 and 1941.

54

PLATE XXVII

EXAMPLES OF BLUE CLEARING FAR FROM OPPOSITION

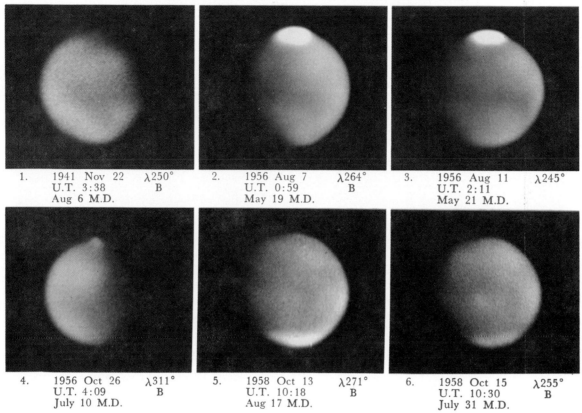

1.	1941 Nov 22	λ250°
	U.T. 3:38	B
	Aug 6 M.D.	

2.	1956 Aug 7	λ264°
	U.T. 0:59	B
	May 19 M.D.	

3.	1956 Aug 11	λ245°
	U.T. 2:11	B
	May 21 M.D.	

4.	1956 Oct 26	λ311°
	U.T. 4:09	B
	July 10 M.D.	

5.	1958 Oct 13	λ271°
	U.T. 10:18	B
	Aug 17 M.D.	

6.	1958 Oct 15	λ255°
	U.T. 10:30	B
	July 31 M.D.	

Plate XXVIII

Further comparative blue photographs made on the same dates at Flagstaff and Bloemfontein show different faces of the planet during a period of one month. Despite the 9-hour difference in longitude, almost all faces of the planet are included in this series. A graphical study of all our blue photographs of the planet over a period of thirty years has revealed that the dark regions show better near the meridian 270°, or near Syrtis Major, than on the opposite side of the planet. Since the majority of the Flagstaff photographs present this view of the planet, it is to be expected that they would tend to show slightly more blue clearing than their Bloemfontein counterparts. Some of the latter, however, also show the more favorable side. Nevertheless, the pair-by-pair comparisons from August 23 to September 23 consistently show greater blue clearing on the Flagstaff photographs than those made at Bloemfontein, and this by a considerable factor. Because of the similar methods used in securing the photographs, the wide difference in the opacity of the Martian atmosphere is quite puzzling.

Naturally it may occur to some readers to question whether the two telescope objectives might differ in their capacity to transmit the shorter wavelengths. However, my experience with the two telescopes convinces me that the advantage, if any, certainly lies with the Lowell telescope in this respect. There is another reason which might account for the observed differences. It is well known that as one goes toward the shorter wavelengths the opacity of the Martian atmosphere increases. The declination of Mars was 10° south of the equator during this period. Therefore, because of the difference in the latitude of the two observatories, the zenith distances of Mars at culmination were 19° and 45° in South Africa and Flagstaff, respectively. For this reason more greenish-blue light would be effective at Flagstaff than at Bloemfontein where more of the violet light would get through the earth's atmosphere. As a result the South African photographs should be richer in the shorter wavelengths of violet light and therefore show less blue clearing. This apparently accounts for the main difference between the two sets of photographs.

In the Flagstaff photographs, VS=V. Slipher, G=Giclas.

FLAGSTAFF SOUTH AFRICA

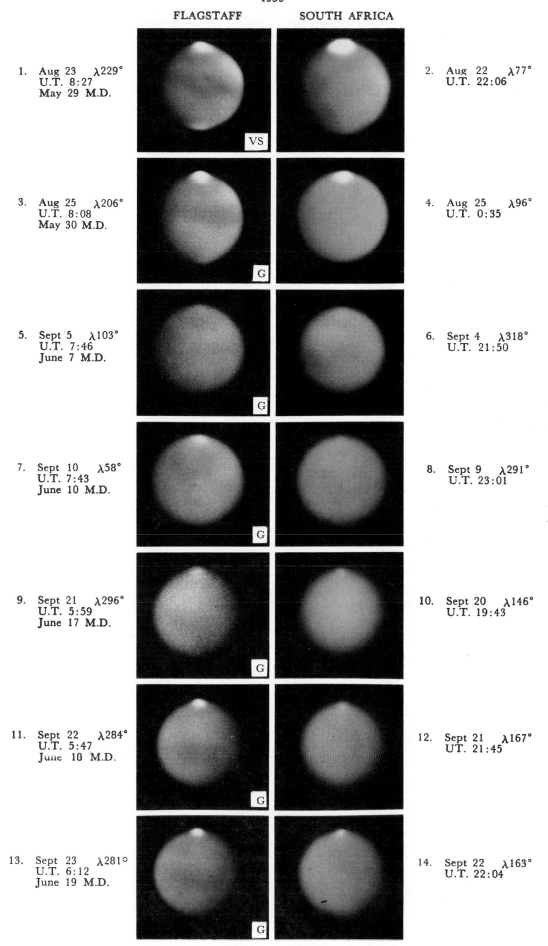

1. Aug 23 λ229°
U.T. 8:27
May 29 M.D.

2. Aug 22 λ77°
U.T. 22:06

3. Aug 25 λ206°
U.T. 8:08
May 30 M.D.

4. Aug 25 λ96°
U.T. 0:35

5. Sept 5 λ103°
U.T. 7:46
June 7 M.D.

6. Sept 4 λ318°
U.T. 21:50

7. Sept 10 λ58°
U.T. 7:43
June 10 M.D.

8. Sept 9 λ291°
U.T. 23:01

9. Sept 21 λ296°
U.T. 5:59
June 17 M.D.

10. Sept 20 λ146°
U.T. 19:43

11. Sept 22 λ284°
U.T. 5:47
June 10 M.D.

12. Sept 21 λ167°
UT. 21:45

13. Sept 23 λ281°
U.T. 6:12
June 19 M.D.

14. Sept 22 λ163°
U.T. 22:04

Plate XXIX

These photographs show changes in the size and form of the Solis Lacus region from 1907 to 1956. In Plates XI, XII, XIII and XIV we have seen various stages in the seasonal changes in the polar caps and dark markings as well as striking secular changes in the Syrtis Major region. In No. 1, taken in 1907, the Solis Lacus consisted of two contiguous dark spots and the following component was more than three times the size of the preceding one, both being nearly circular in shape. In 1909 the north-south width of the Solis became quite small and showed below the canals Nectar, Tithonius and Bathys as a loop.

Two years later the Solis had much the same shape, but as the photograph shows, had darkened considerably. At the 1926 opposition it had become greatly enlarged and its shape had strikingly changed. It had developed markedly towards the north with the darkest portion being to the north and much below its position in the earlier oppositions. In 1939 and 1941 the dark northern portion had completely disappeared and returned again to about the brightness of the desert leaving the Solis in the shape of a crown of three or four dark knots above what was the darkest area of 1926. In 1954 and 1956, the Solis again resembled its appearance in 1909 and 1911 but differed noticeably in the arrangement of the three or four knots of which it was composed.

In the intervening oppositions the region has otherwise varied in form and size. These variations show that, from time to time, various portions of the Solis Lacus may fade from very intense dark spots to the same brightness as the surrounding desert area.

58

PLATE XXIX
CHANGES IN SOLIS LACUS

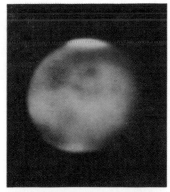

1.   1907 July 28   λ107°
U.T. 8:25 Apr 22 M.D. Y

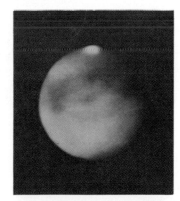

2.   1909 Oct 21   λ93°
July 12 M.D.   Y

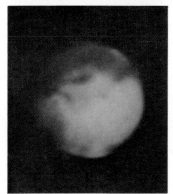

3.   1911 Nov 15   λ100°
Aug 22 M.D.   Y

4.   1926 Nov 22   λ96°
U.T. 4:12 Aug 16 M.D. Y

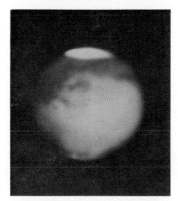

5.   1939 July 22   λ96°
U.T. 22:14 Apr 21 M.D. Y

6.   1941 Nov 4   λ82°
U.T. 5:22 July 28 M.D. Y

7.   1954 July 2   λ65°
U.T. 21:01 Mar 30 M.D. O

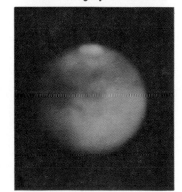

8.   1956 Aug 27   λ78°
U.T. 0:35 May 31 M.D. R

Plate XXX

In addition to the seasonal development of the dark markings, from time to time during the last half century or more, various features have sometimes undergone striking changes which bear little or no relation to the planet's season and are purely secular in nature. A few examples of this type of change are illustrated by this series of images.

For example, at the beginning of the century photograph No. 1 accurately represents the normal coast line of the Mare Cimmerium and Mare Tyrrhenum but in 1924 a dark area began to develop in the desert below Sinus Gomer between the Mare and the Elysium. This development was rather weak at first but grew stronger in 1926 and by 1939, as shown in No. 2, the dark area took on the aspect of permanency and has continued, with some variations, ever since. Likewise the Nepenthes-Thoth system on the forward side of the Syrtis Major was very weak and difficult to see in 1907 but from 1911 on it has been an easy object. From 1916 to the present time this system of canals generally has been so strong as to rival the grosser features of the disk.

Nos. 3 and 4 demonstrate a change of a different type around Laestrygonum Sinus. The Cimmerium above the Laestrygonum has brightened with the bay standing out as a small island connected to the Mare above by two or three canals. Above and to the left near Atlantis is another bright patch on a 1939 photograph which proved to be temporary and evidently represented a cloudy area.

Nos. 5 and 6 show the aspect of the Nepenthes-Thoth in 1909 and in 1928. In 1909 the Nepenthes and Lucus Moeris were strong and dark next to the Syrtis Major, but the Thoth canal itself was weak and nearly invisible. However, in 1928 the Thoth appears extremely broad and dark, consisting of a series of recognizable markings. Running through the mass of detail and a little to the right of the center is a canal-like core bordered on the outside by a series of spots and irregular details, while the inside edge is lined by a hazy border. At the base are two oases with two short canals running northward into the polar collar.

The southern Aethiopis shows a V-shaped mass of intricate dark markings too complex to decipher in detail. Comparative photographs of other oppositions from 1916 to the present reveal that many changes are occurring in this general area.

The three photographs at the bottom of the page, taken in 1907, 1939 and 1954, demonstrate quite clearly the enormous changes which have taken place in the desert region from the Syrtis Major to the Elysium. In addition to the development below Sinus Gomer, we see changes in 1939 in the Thoth-Nepenthes system and to the left of the Wedge of Casius. We also see in 1954 the development of a large irregular dark area to the left of the Thoth in the general region of the Nodus Lacoontis. Early symptoms of this change were indicated by photographs of the region taken in 1952, but this new dark area reached its maximum development two years later. Except for slight variations, it is still present.

From this series of changes we are forced to conclude that regions which appear to belong to maria and are therefore dark areas may change into desert areas, and by the same token, areas which first become familiar as desert regions may at another time become dark regions.

In Nos. 1 and 7, PL=Percival Lowell.

PLATE XXX

PHOTOGRAPHS DISPLAYING SECULAR CHANGES IN THE DARK MARKINGS

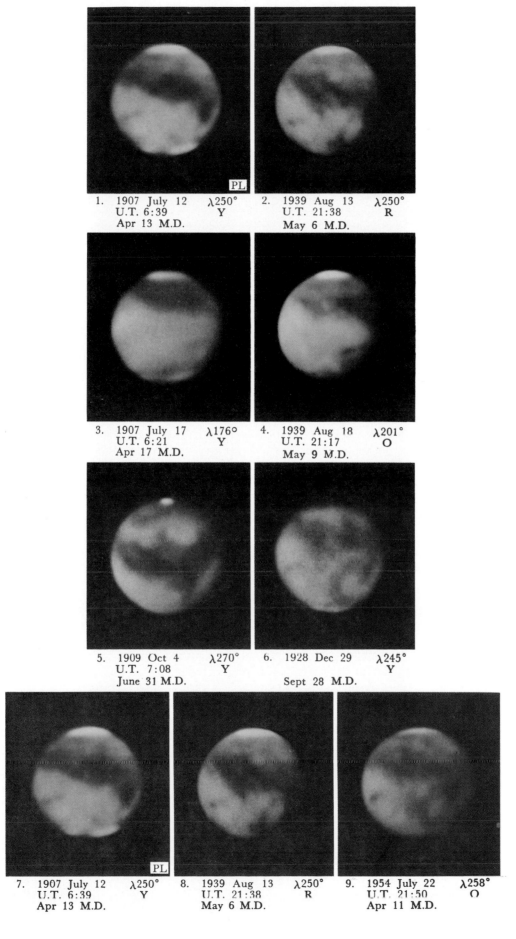

1. 1907 July 12   λ250°
    U.T. 6:39   Y
    Apr 13 M.D.

2. 1939 Aug 13   λ250°
    U.T. 21:38   R
    May 6 M.D.

3. 1907 July 17   λ176°
    U.T. 6:21   Y
    Apr 17 M.D.

4. 1939 Aug 18   λ201°
    U.T. 21:17   O
    May 9 M.D.

5. 1909 Oct 4   λ270°
    U.T. 7:08   Y
    June 31 M.D.

6. 1928 Dec 29   λ245°
                   Y
    Sept 28 M.D.

7. 1907 July 12   λ250°
    U.T. 6:39   Y
    Apr 13 M.D.

8. 1939 Aug 13   λ250°
    U.T. 21:38   R
    May 6 M.D.

9. 1954 July 22   λ258°
    U.T. 21:50   O
    Apr 11 M.D.

Plate XXXI

These drawings made from visual observations may readily be compared with photographs of the same aspect of the planet. The drawings were made at the Lick, Meudon and Lowell Observatories and the photographs were made at Lowell. Careful comparison of the five different sets of observations will disclose remarkable agreement between the best photographs and the drawings and also notable disagreements when the seeing was poor.

For the first pair (Nos. 1 and 2) Mars was near aphelion (apparent diameter 12″.95) and the magnification of the image was equivalent to 1800 diameters. Despite the severe loss of detail resulting from image composition to reduce graininess, enough remains to verify the existence of most of the details in the drawings. Careful study of the original plate shows traces of virtually everything seen visually.

No. 3, a drawing by Trumpler using the Lick 36-inch refractor on October 23, 1926, is substantially confirmed by my photograph, No. 4, of the same general region on November 22. Close comparison discloses that traces of most of the canals and oases on the drawing are corroborated by traces of similar detail in the photograph.

Comparison of the Antoniadi drawing, No. 5, with my photograph of the same region, No. 6, (magnification 1700 diameters) reveals that all the numerous details in the photograph to the left of and above the Thoth, namely in the Aethiopis and Elysium regions, are not recorded in his drawing. However, his representation of the aspect of the Thoth itself is not supported by the photograph. Examples are the short double canal running downward from the base of the Thoth, and also the dark, core-like medial line through the center of the Thoth flanked by diffuse irregular shadings on each side.

No. 7, is a circular section copied from Trumpler's 1924 map of the planet which is compared with our 1941 photograph, No. 8. A careful comparison should disclose that many of the finer details of his map are identifiable in the photograph, in particular many of the details in the southern part of the disk above the Sabaeus Sinus. The many fine traceries and spots in his map are faintly revealed in the original photograph, although the observations are separated by fifteen years.

No. 9 is a drawing by the author. Photograph No. 10 was made a little later and shows the same face of the planet as Nos. 5 and 6. Here the agreement between drawing and photograph is more satisfactory and the one corroborates the other in a substantial manner. The markings missing in Antoniadi's drawing should be apparent in our drawing and photograph. Astronomers who observe the planet both visually and photographically know that nearly every detail observed visually can be found on some of the photographs, but the latter may show only a trace of something without clearly revealing its character or appearance. The visual observations have been of great help in the representation of the fine structure, such as sharpness, width and regularity of boundary lines or canals. On the other hand many markings are quite satisfactorily shown by the photographs which were not noticed in the visual observations. Those experienced in both types of observations fully realize the photograph may not show the precise character of extremely minute markings, but with regard to the reality of controversial markings, the evidence of the photograph is undeniable.

PLATE XXXI
COMPARISON OF DRAWINGS AND PHOTOGRAPHS

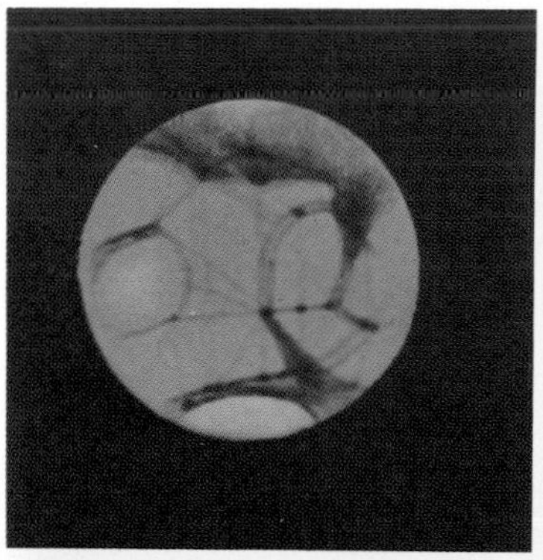

1. 1916 Feb 11
   (Slipher drawing)
   Nov 15 M.D.

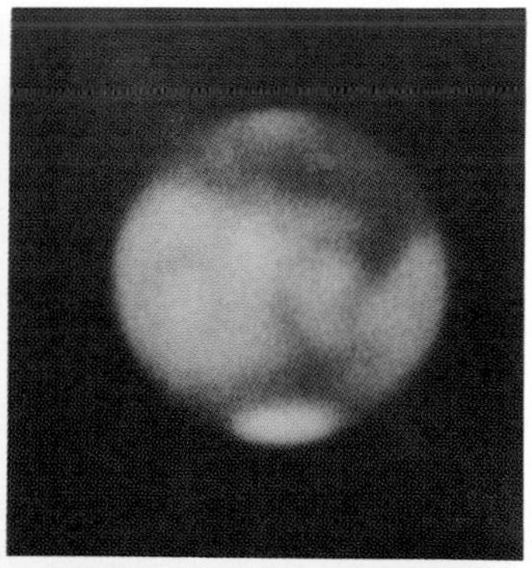

2. 1916 Feb 12   λ250°
   U.T. 4:26   Y
   Nov 15 M.D.

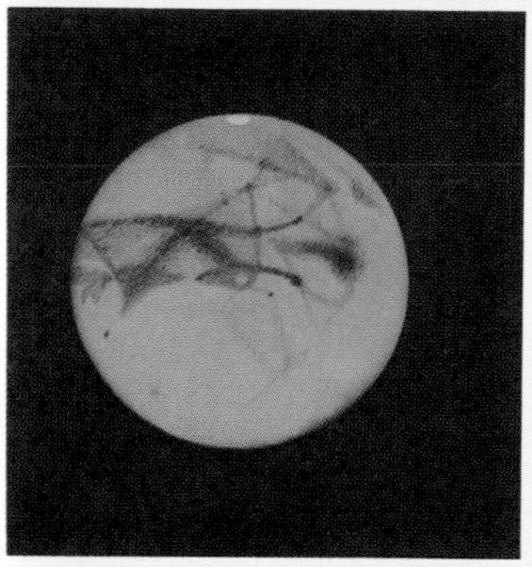

3. 1926 Oct 23
   (Trumpler drawing)
   July 30 M.D.

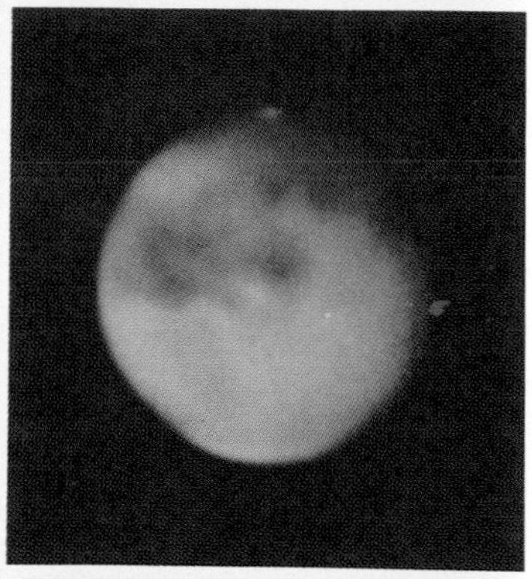

4. 1926 Nov 22   λ96°
   U.T. 4:12   Y
   Aug 16 M.D.

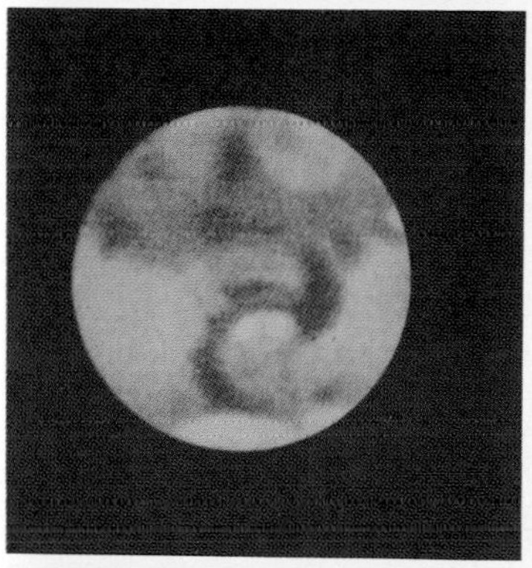

5. 1928 Dec 15
   (Antoniadi drawing)
   Sept 21 M.D.

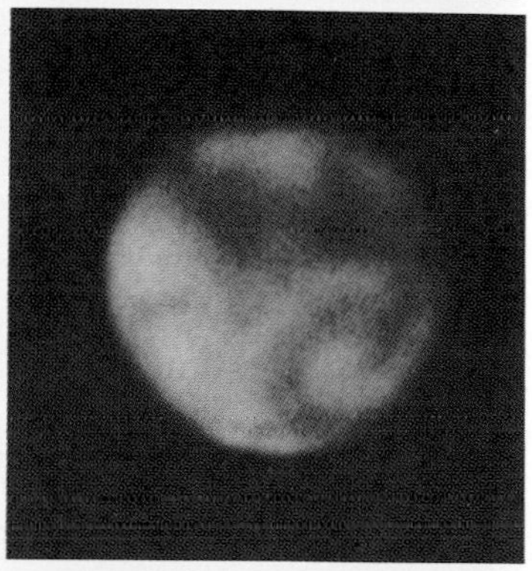

6. 1928 Dec 29   λ245°
   Sept 28 M.D.   Y

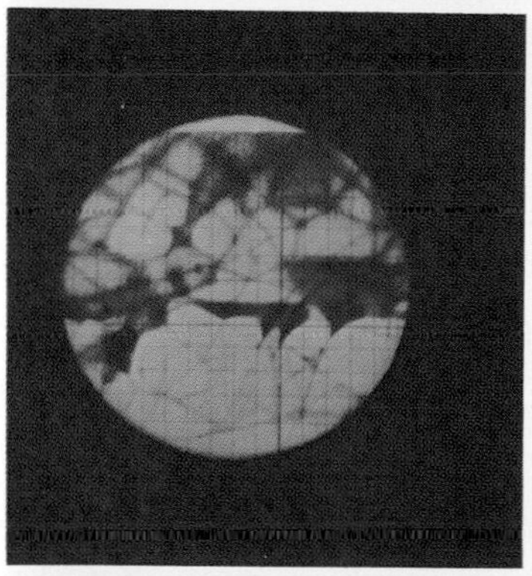

7. 1924 Trumpler Map

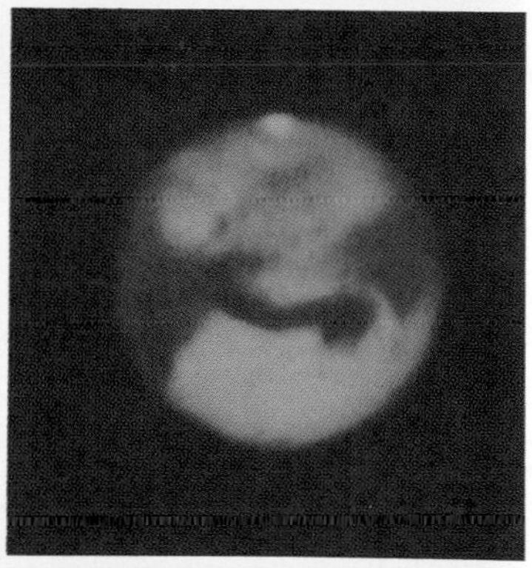

8. 1941 Oct 11   λ338°
   U.T. 8:06   R
   July 11 M.D.

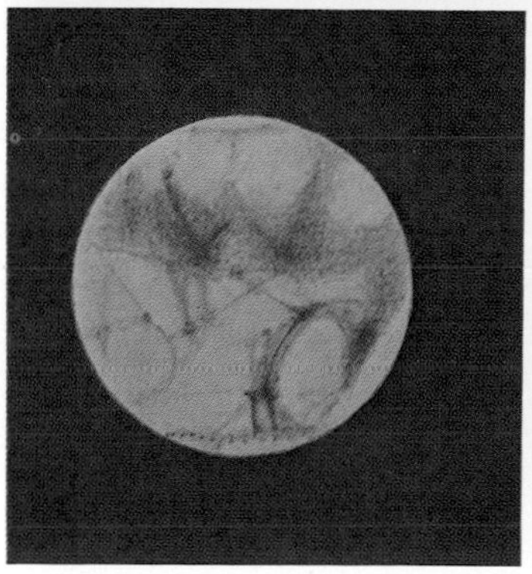

9. 1928 Dec 28
   (Slipher Drawing)
   Sept 28 M.D.

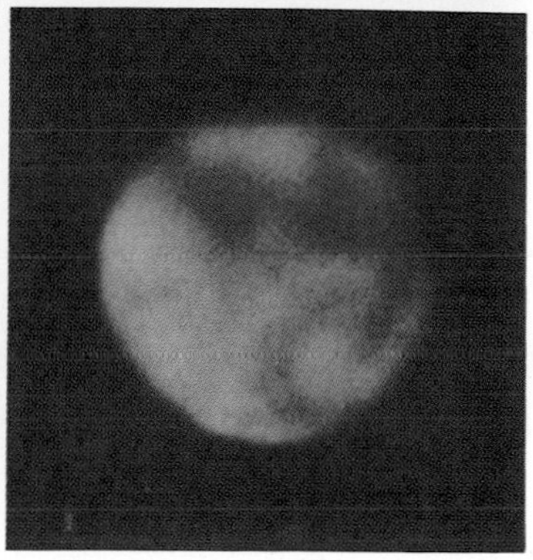

10. 1928 Dec 29   λ245°
    Sept 28 M.D.   Y

Plate XXXII

Although band-like streaks of haze have sometimes appeared faintly on our blue photographs, the photographs on June 14 and July 18, 1954, surprisingly showed five or six alternate bright and dark bands across the face of the planet. This belted pattern is clear over much of the disk, but shows especially well across the large bright area on the forenoon (right) side of No. 1. This position indicates that the belted pattern is at a higher level than the bright area. On the afternoon side of the disk the pattern appears disrupted and destroyed, as if by convection in the region of the equator. Photograph No. 2 displays a similar set of belts when the same face of the planet came into view about a month later. Surface features shown in Nos. 1 and 2 include the Syrtis Major and much of the dark maria. Significantly these surface features are visible in the dark bands but are concealed by the bright belts.

"Weather bands" in Nos. 1 and 2 roughly parallel the planet's equator. In Nos. 3 and 4, the haze bands angling steeply across the planet's equator are more in line with the motions of yellow clouds (which have been observed) over the Martian tropics. These novel weather bands, or similar ones, appear faintly for several nights in our 1954 blue photographs around longitude 210°. Later in this opposition the Martian air became more or less uniformly opaque over these regions and the bands vanished.

In 1926, when No. 3 was taken, some faint bands running at a 45° angle with the equator were detected near longitude 20°. In 1952 an excellent blue photograph near longitude 180°, obtained by Humason with the Palomar 200-inch reflector, displays striking parallel streamers across the disk tilted 135° to the equator.

In No. 5 the blue photograph shows a unique aspect of the violet layer. All of Mars, except the polar caps, was masked by a peculiar mosaic mottle somewhat like a mackerel sky. This pattern is in strong contrast to the long streamers and weather bands exhibited in the photographs above. Whether this banded effect was also present around longitude 290° we have no way of knowing because that region was inaccessible at Bloemfontein and the Flagstaff observations were then centered around 190°.

The blue photograph in No. 6 shows still another typical example of the behavior of the planet's atmosphere. The violet layer is here so opaque to blue light as to obliterate all the surface detail except the snow cap at the south pole, and of course no bands are visible.

The various phenomena pointed out here, being solely atmospheric features, are readily penetrated by the longer wavelengths of light and therefore are completely invisible in red photographs.

64

PLATE XXXII

MARS FOR THE FIRST TIME REVEALS ATMOSPHERIC BELTS

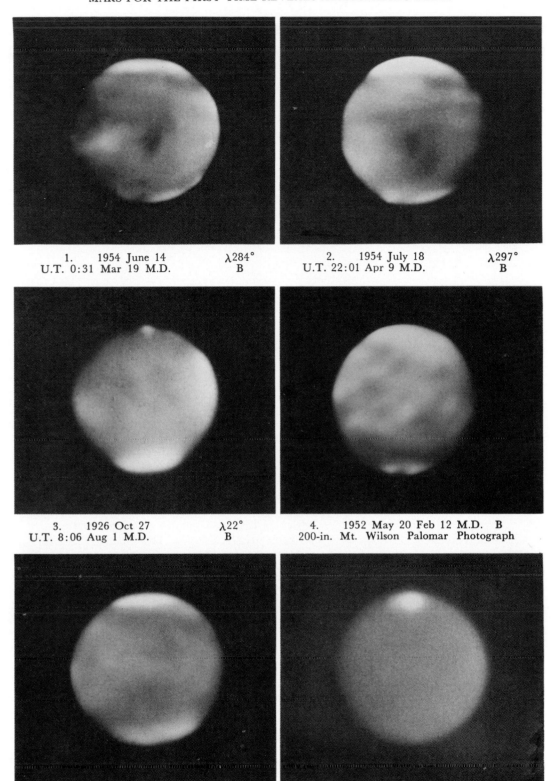

1.   1954 June 14   λ284°
U.T. 0:31 Mar 19 M.D.   B

2.   1954 July 18   λ297°
U.T. 22:01 Apr 9 M.D.   B

3.   1926 Oct 27   λ22°
U.T. 8:06 Aug 1 M.D.   B

4.   1952 May 20 Feb 12 M.D.   B
200-in. Mt. Wilson Palomar Photograph

5.   1954 July 4   λ74'
U.T. 22:53 Mar 31 M.D.   B

6.   1956 Aug 23   λ75°
U.T. 23:09 May 30 M.D.   B

Plate XXXIII

The new type of markings discussed on this page are among the most interesting phenomena observed since the discovery of seasonal changes on Mars. During the height of the great storm in 1956 a series of transitory dark spots was observed to be associated with some of the denser masses of clouds. At first most observers did not attach any special significance to the phenomenon. Visual observers, who made reference to them, appear to have attributed the dark spots merely to areas of the planet's surface showing through gaps between the clouds. However, the photograph clearly shows that the dark areas are darker than the bare surface would appear and are in fact darker than any other markings on the disk, even Sabaeus Sinus, Dawes Bay or the Mare Erythraeum.

The first six photographs on the page vividly display the changing form and location of a series of such temporary dark areas in the southern part of the disk on August 29, 30 and 31 and on September 1, 3 and 5. In the first four, the dark patch was distinctly darker than the rest of the disk, and therefore represented something different from ordinary markings. In photographs 5 and 6 the intensity of the temporary dark areas was not greater than it would be if they were seen between clouds. Their association with the dark areas on the other photographs, however, suggests that they too owed their existence to the same origin. The two photographs, Nos. 7 and 8, show the normal appearance of the same faces of Mars without the storm clouds and without the strange dark areas. These two photographs do not reveal any suggestion of the intense isolated dark spots in the first six images. The intimate association of the variable dark areas with storm clouds and their ephemeral nature strongly indicates that they came from something released by the clouds. The close resemblance between these dark patches and the dark collar (Plate XVII) which always borders the melting polar caps suggests a like origin, the presence of water and moistened soil. The short-lived character of this series of dark spots, lasting only a matter of hours at most, does not militate against this hypothesis.

But whatever the true explanation of these temporary features of the surface, their peculiar character and close resemblance to the other dark markings stamps them of special significance.

Since the most important and significant change observed on Mars is the wave of darkening that sweeps over the dark regions of the summer hemisphere, the sudden outbreak of these dark bluish areas in Martian June, whatever the cause, interpose an interesting problem that requires explanation.

66

PLATE XXXIII

NEW TYPE TEMPORARY DARK MARKINGS COMPARED (BOTTOM ROW) WITH NORMAL.

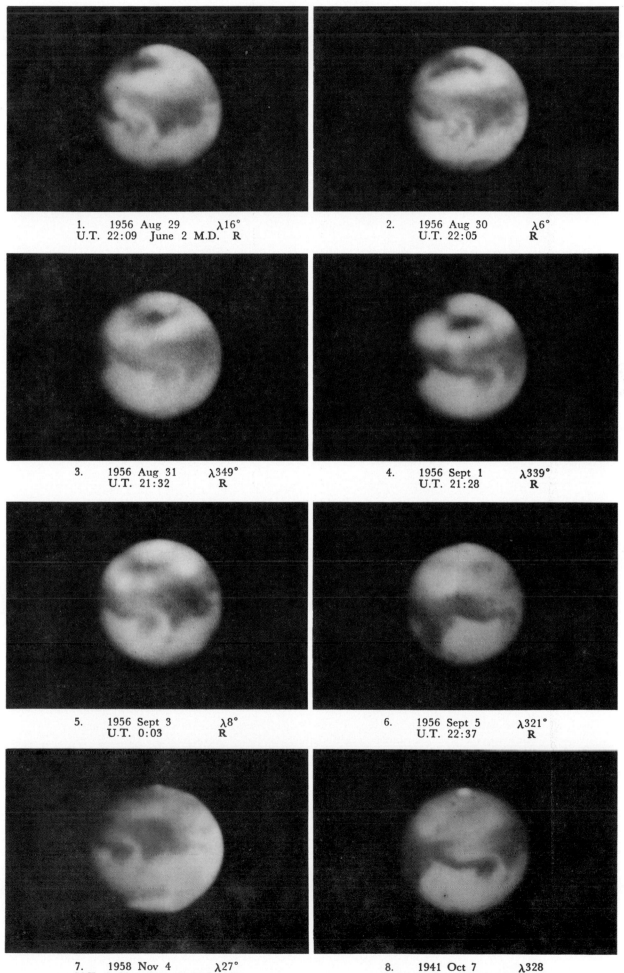

1.　　1956 Aug 29　　λ16°
U.T. 22:09　June 2 M.D.　R

2.　　1956 Aug 30　　λ6°
U.T. 22:05　　　　　　R

3.　　1956 Aug 31　　λ349°
U.T. 21:32　　　　　　R

4.　　1956 Sept 1　　λ339°
U.T. 21:28　　　　　　R

5.　　1956 Sept 3　　λ8°
U.T. 0:03　　　　　　R

6.　　1956 Sept 5　　λ321°
U.T. 22:37　　　　　　R

7.　　1958 Nov 4　　λ27°
U.T. 7:02　Aug 11 M.D.　Y

8.　　1941 Oct 7　　λ328
U.T. 5:16　July 9 M.D.　R

Plate XXXIV

Plate XXXIV includes photographs obtained between 1905 and 1963, together with drawings intended to help the reader identify the linear markings or "canals". All drawings were made in 1963 by Pat Bridges, scientific illustrator for the Aeronautical Chart and Information Center's lunar mapping facility at the Lowell Observatory. She had no previous knowledge of Martian features and merely drew what she saw in the photographs. With the exception of a single line (see No. 2 below), all features recorded by Mrs. Bridges have been confirmed either by inspection of Martian maps, or visually by astronomers at the telescope at the time the photographs were made.

No. 1. This single image is one of several obtained by C. O. Lampland and described in detail in Lowell Bulletin No. 21 by Percival Lowell and Lampland (see also Plate XIII No. 1). No. 2. The photograph, from a plate by E. C. Slipher, has many more features and shows the advantage of compositing; four images were used. One line (just below left of center in photograph) has been deleted from the drawing because it was found to be caused by a strong blemish in one of the four images. No. 3. A composite of three images from a plate by E. C. Slipher is shown at left. No. 4. A composite of 12 images from a plate taken by H. L. Giclas and S. E. Jones shows two dark markings within the dark area of Casius which were seen at the telescope by both observers. It is interesting that this photograph was taken at a very unfavorable opposition when the Martian disk subtended only 14 seconds of arc.

Doubtless the latitude of the observer has had much to do with seeing the lines. Since all the closest approaches of the planet occur near perihelion when the declination of Mars is far south of our equator; for stations in high northern latitudes, observations can only be made under very difficult conditions. It is for this reason that a Lowell astronomer observed Mars in Chile in 1907 and in Bloemfontein, South Africa, in 1939, 1954, and 1956.

Curiously, the 'anti-canalists' declare that they can see canals only when the seeing is not very good, and furthermore, that the canals disappear when the seeing becomes excellent. At such times, it is alleged, small spots or markings appear which may be in a more or less linear array. I have never seen or photographed the breakup of linear markings into spotted line-like arrays as the seeing became superb.

The reader must bear in mind that the canals can change markedly from thin line-like features to broad bands. Examples of this phenomenon are Nilokeros, Ganges, Aethiops, Amenthes and Thoth. The bands sometimes appear as irregular streaks or spotted areas, which are gross features when compared to the relatively fine lines found at other times in the same regions.

Photographs have recorded traces of most of the canals and oases in the same positions as those drawn on the Lowell maps and on Trumpler's[1] aerographic maps of the planet compiled mostly from photographs made at the Lick Observatory.

[1]Trumpler, R. J., 1927, Lick Obs. Bull., *13*, 387.

PLATE XXXIV
PHOTOGRAPHS AND CORRESPONDING DRAWINGS 1905 - 1963

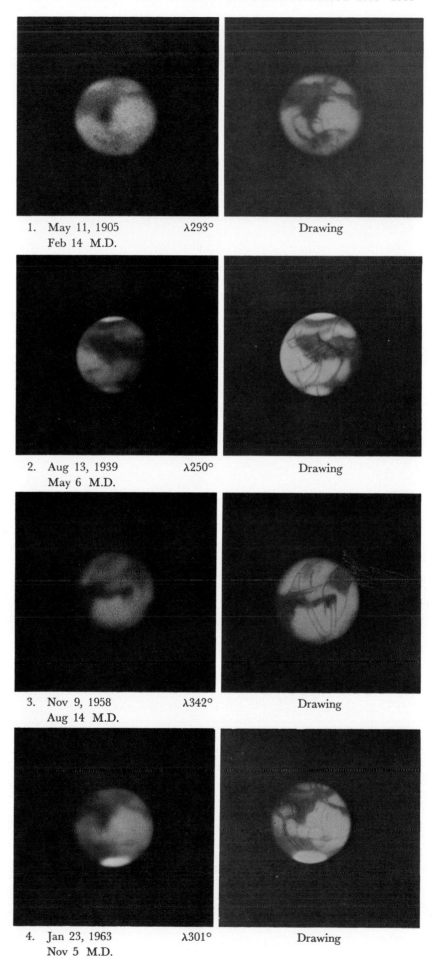

1. May 11, 1905   λ293°   Drawing
    Feb 14 M.D.

2. Aug 13, 1939   λ250°   Drawing
    May 6 M.D.

3. Nov 9, 1958   λ342°   Drawing
    Aug 14 M.D.

4. Jan 23, 1963   λ301°   Drawing
    Nov 5 M.D.

Plate XXXV

A group of eight red photographs taken at the 1956 opposition of Mars shows the appearance of various faces of the planet. In some of these, clouds covered parts of the southern hemisphere and greatly altered the normal appearance of the familiar dark areas while in others, such as Nos. 4, 5 and 6, the Martian sky was nearly clear so that the dark regions appeared nearly normal. In Nos. 1, 2 and 3 a heavy cloud canopy covered much of the southern hemisphere with its lower boundary consisting of a series of semicircular curves or scallops. This canopy concealed the surface and also nearly hid the south cap. At the same time, however, an unusual dark spot stood out at a different place and with a different shape each night. (These ephemeral dark areas and their significance are also discussed in connection with Plate XXXIII.)

In No. 1 it will be seen that cloud over Fastigium Aryn makes Dawes Bay almost unrecognizable while thin haze over Pandorae Fretum veils it perceptibly. In No. 2 scattered clouds in this same region cause a broken appearance to Dawes Bay and to that general area. No. 7, taken before the cloudy period began, represents about the normal aspect of the Syrtis Major region as can be judged by the clarity of the south cap. No. 8 shows heavy obscuration from Sabaeus Sinus southward due to haze and clouds; even the south cap is all but concealed, while the Pandorae Fretum and the Mare Erythraeum on the right are markedly dimmed. Hellas is completely cloud covered and stands out as the brightest region on the whole disk.

PLATE XXXV

SERIES SHOWING COMPLETE CIRCUIT OF MARS

1956

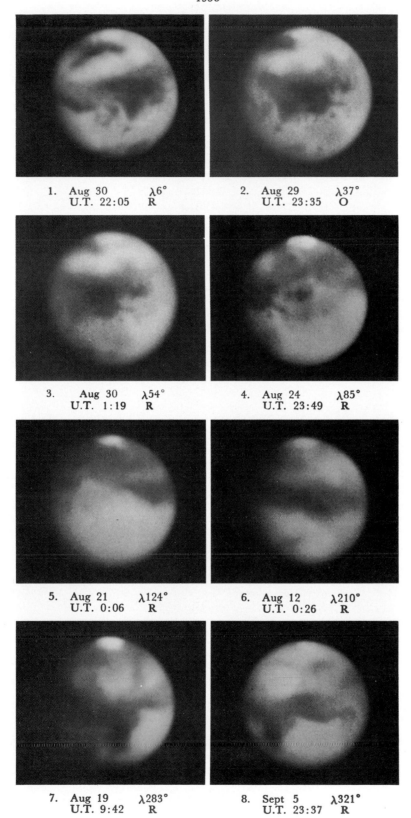

1. Aug 30   λ6°
    U.T. 22:05   R

2. Aug 29   λ37°
    U.T. 23:35   O

3.   Aug 30   λ54°
    U.T. 1:19   R

4. Aug 24   λ85°
    U.T. 23:49   R

5. Aug 21   λ124°
    U.T. 0:06   R

6. Aug 12   λ210°
    U.T. 0:26   R

7. Aug 19   λ283°
    U.T. 9:42   R

8. Sept 5   λ321°
    U.T. 23:37   R

Plate XXXVI

The 1963 opposition being near apogee, the apparent size of Mars was never greater than 14″ of arc. Martian dates given on this plate have been computed for the planet's northern hemisphere rather than for the southern hemisphere, which is customarily used for apogee oppositions. On the yellow photograph in No. 1 the Wedge of Casius area is large and conspicuous. The Nilotis is easily recognizable extending north towards the Nilo Syrtis from the tip of the Syrtis Major. The Ismenius Lacus is seen to the west. In No. 2 a double cloud covers the Mare Acidalium on the sunrise limb. In No. 3 Euximus, Castrorius and Propontis I and II are prominently darkened. The Trivium is the dark marking to right of center. The two evening clouds on the blue photograph in No. 4 are about 40° east of the Mare Acidalium; the north one is so strong it can be discerned on the yellow photograph of the same date.

In the yellow photograph (No. 5) the tip of the Margaritifer is hidden by a cloud opaque to this wavelength region. The area from the southeast edge of Mare Acidalium to the Lacus Lunae is filled in. The same bright clouds seen in the blue photograph of No. 6 may be seen on the yellow photograph. The density and behavior of these clouds are very similar to ones photographed on February 7, 1931. In No. 7 the yellow photograph shows yellow cloud distribution over the same areas that show heavy clouds in the blue photograph two nights later in No. 6. The Solis Lacus can be seen in the upper right. The Nectar and Agathadaemon form connecting bridges to the larger dark areas. Comparison of No. 8 with No. 4 shows the persistence of the double cloud patterns seen in blue photographs two days earlier.

PLATE XXXVI
MARS DURING 1963 OPPOSITION

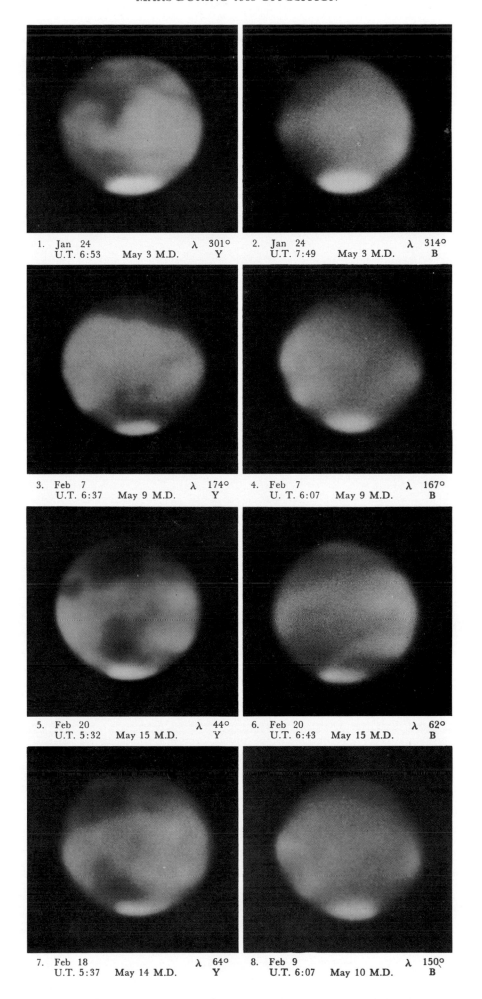

1. Jan 24   λ 301°
   U.T. 6:53   May 3 M.D.   Y

2. Jan 24   λ 314°
   U.T. 7:49   May 3 M.D.   B

3. Feb 7   λ 174°
   U.T. 6:37   May 9 M.D.   Y

4. Feb 7   λ 167°
   U. T. 6:07   May 9 M.D.   B

5. Feb 20   λ 44°
   U.T. 5:32   May 15 M.D.   Y

6. Feb 20   λ 62°
   U.T. 6:43   May 15 M.D.   B

7. Feb 18   λ 64°
   U.T. 5:37   May 14 M.D.   Y

8. Feb 9   λ 150°
   U.T. 6:07   May 10 M.D.   B

Plate XXXVII

Plate XXXVII shows six examples of yellow photographs of Jupiter taken from 1904 to 1909 displaying the great symmetry and distinctness of the belts. Images showing as many as ten belts with numerous spots and other finer details, as in the 1909 photographs, denote a surprisingly high degree of resolution in these early pictures.

Since this is the first plate in the Jupiter series, it is perhaps appropriate to remind the reader of the statement given in the introductory material. "The longitudes of the central meridian (λ) for both Mars and Jupiter were computed from the values tabulated in the *American Ephemeris and Nautical Almanac* in the section designated as *Ephemerides for Physical Observations*." For Jupiter's longitude System II was used.

PLATE XXXVII

YELLOW FILTER PHOTOGRAPHS DISPLAYING THE BELTS 1904 - 1909.

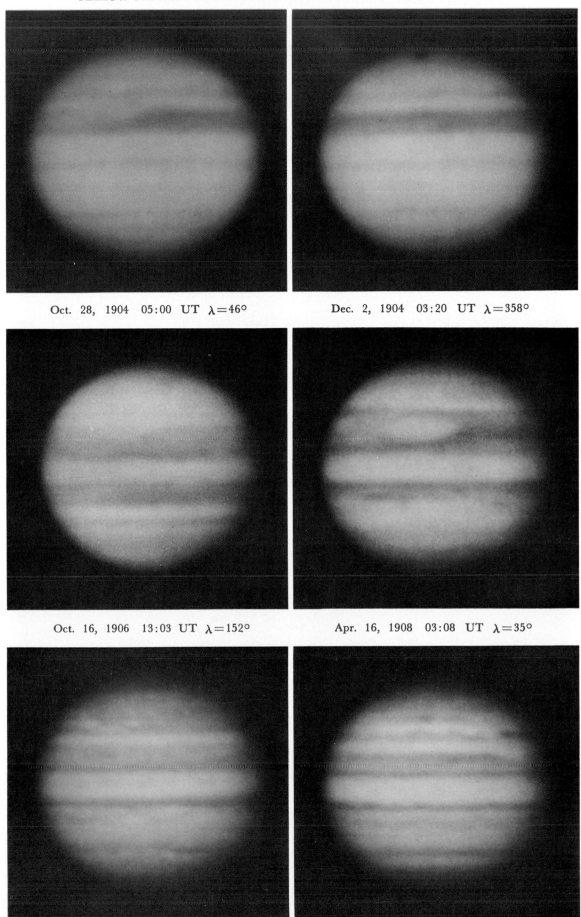

Oct. 28, 1904 05:00 UT λ=46°   Dec. 2, 1904 03:20 UT λ=358°

Oct. 16, 1906 13:03 UT λ=152°   Apr. 16, 1908 03:08 UT λ=35°

Apr. 28, 1909 02:45 UT λ=123°   Apr. 27, 1909 02:52 UT λ=337°

Plate XXXVIII

The yellow photographs in Plate XXXVIII display some of the longest observed and best known markings on Jupiter. Thus, in 1909 we see the South Tropical Disturbance above the center; and on May 6, 1911, September 21, 1913, and August 17, 1913, and September 3, 1914, the large oval marking above the middle marks the famous Great Red Spot, observed since 1664. The September 21, 1913 image displays numerous dark wisps across the Equatorial Zone. Also on September 3 and September 24, 1914, is shown a peculiar pattern of port-hole markings below the equator; while a shadow of Satellite III is visible on the last image.

PLATE XXXVIII

YELLOW FILTER PHOTOGRAPHS DISPLAYING THE BELTS 1909 - 1914.

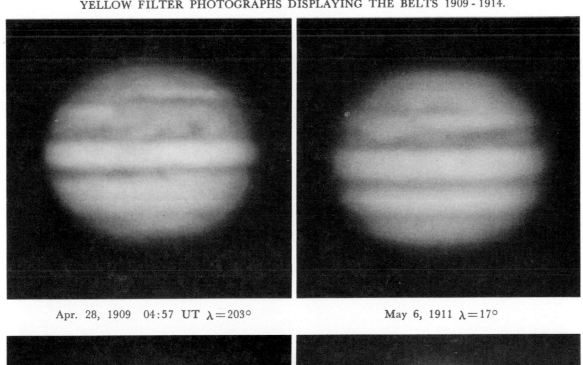

Apr. 28, 1909   04:57 UT λ = 203°

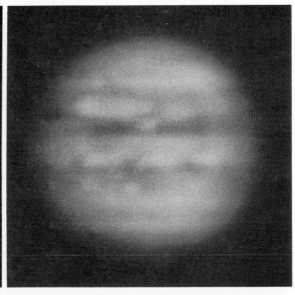

May 6, 1911 λ = 17°

Sep. 21, 1913   02:29 UT λ = 269°

Aug. 17, 1913 λ = 270°

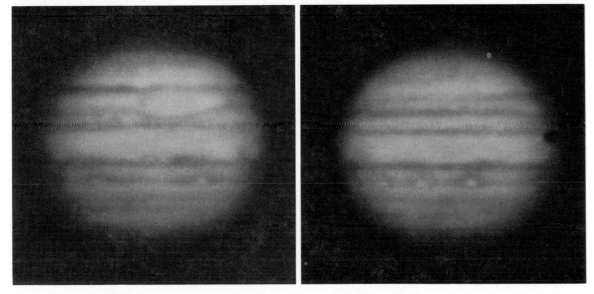

Sep. 3, 1914   03:24 UT λ = 218°

Sep. 24, 1914   03:12 UT λ = 129°

Plate XXXIX

The photographs in Plate XXXIX show a wide variety of markings and a remarkable wealth of detail especially in the first five images, including delicate wisps, distinct dark and white spots, and the sharp breaks in the South Equatorial Belt. The bay of the Red Spot is visible on images Nos. 2, 3 and 5. In the March 8 photograph we witness the complete breaking up of the South Equatorial Belt into isolated spots. However, photographs taken in May 1920 show that the South Equatorial Belt had regained its normal form and appearance.

PLATE XXXIX
YELLOW FILTER PHOTOGRAPHS DISPLAYING THE BELTS 1915 - 1920.

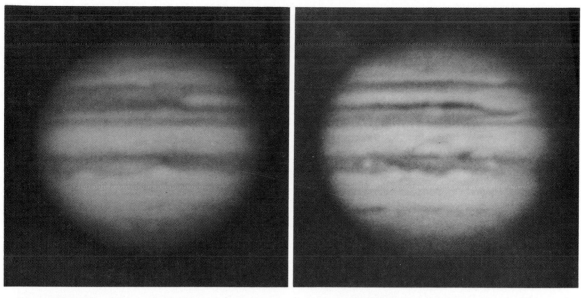

Oct. 19, 1915   03:15 UT $\lambda = 15°$ Oct. 20, 1915   02:21 UT $\lambda = 133°$

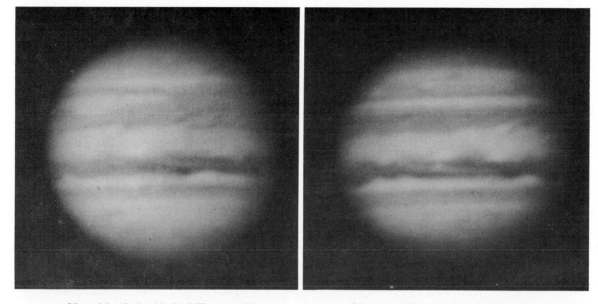

Nov. 26, 1916   02:04 UT $\lambda = 168°$ Nov. 30, 1916   01:30 UT $\lambda = 29°$

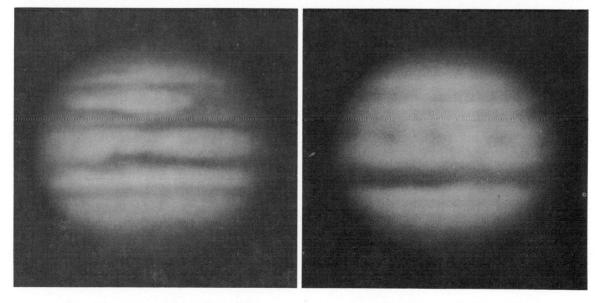

Dec. 20, 1917   06:53 UT $\lambda = 80°$ Mar. 8, 1920   05:34 UT $\lambda = 214°$

Plate XL

The photographs in Plate XL display many changes in the surface markings from the nearly blank appearance of the South Tropical region in 1926 and 1927 images—an appearance closely resembling the general aspect in 1936 and 1937 (Plate XLI) and in 1919. A condition of great activity there is denoted by the series of dark and bright spots shown in the 1928 photograph.

80

PLATE XL

YELLOW FILTER PHOTOGRAPHS DISPLAYING THE BELTS 1920 - 1928.

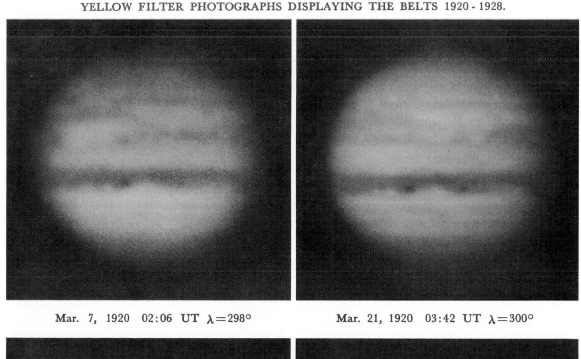

Mar. 7, 1920   02:06 UT $\lambda = 298°$ Mar. 21, 1920   03:42 UT $\lambda = 300°$

Mar. 29, 1921   07:09 UT $\lambda = 284°$ Aug. 15, 1926   07:31 UT $\lambda = 177°$

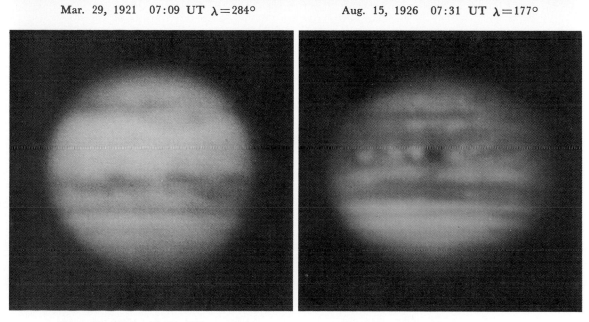

Nov. 20, 1927   03:24 UT $\lambda = 341°$ Nov. 24, 1928   06:26 UT $\lambda = 214°$

Plate XLI

In Plate XLI yellow-filter photographs reveal a series of changes in both equatorial belts, the Red Spot, and in the width and markings of the Equatorial Zone itself. Evident changes in the width and intensity of the belts are obvious by mere inspection; the Equatorial Zone in 1938 was invaded by dark material and broad wisps, while a comparison of the Red Spot in 1931, 1936, 1937 shows that it greatly darkened (became reddish). In 1938 the Red Spot was bright again and shows as an ellipse. In 1933 the South Tropical Disturbance is seen at central meridian, much altered from its appearance in the earlier years. Note that while the Red Spot was unusually red in 1936 and 1937, the Southern Equatorial Belt had disappeared and the region was bright, but with the revival of activity in 1938[1] the belt re-formed again. Also note the isolated dark bar in the north edge of the North Equatorial Belt resembling one in nearly the same position in 1937.

[1]Slipher, E. C., 1938, P.A.S.P., *9*, 167.

PLATE XLI

YELLOW FILTER PHOTOGRAPHS DISPLAYING THE BELTS 1931 - 1938.

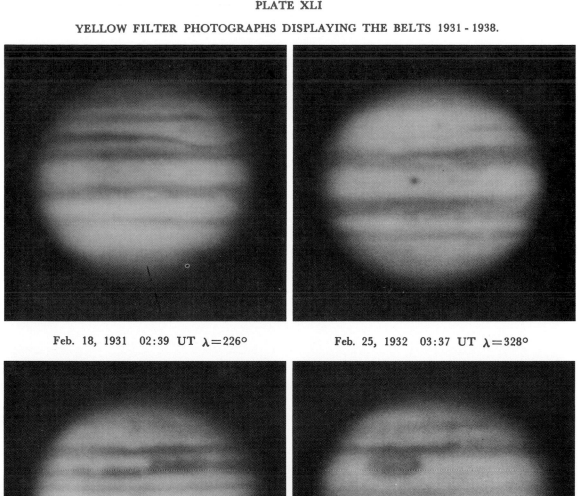

Feb. 18, 1931   02:39 UT $\lambda = 226°$ Feb. 25, 1932   03:37 UT $\lambda = 328°$

Apr. 27, 1933   04:46 UT $\lambda = 65°$ Jul. 5, 1936   07:13 UT $\lambda = 167°$

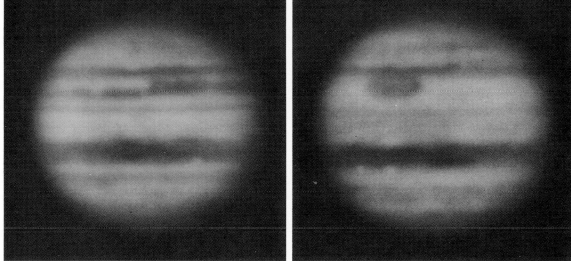

Jul. 16, 1937   07:40 UT $\lambda = 131°$ Aug. 11, 1938   06:57 UT $\lambda = 148°$

Plate XLII

In Plate XLII are samples of yellow photographs obtained from 1939 to 1956, a period characterized by a series of major transformations involving almost the whole disk of Jupiter. Features varied from the strong belts as illustrated by the images of 1939 and 1948, fading to the extremely blank condition of the Equatorial Zone and South Equatorial Belt as displayed in 1940 and 1952. Note the very intense, sharply defined markings in the North Equatorial Belt in 1943. The Red Spot is very pale in both the 1948 and 1956 photographs, and is notable on the former date chiefly by its chrysalis, but on the latter date by its bay.

84

PLATE XLII

YELLOW FILTER PHOTOGRAPHS DISPLAYING THE BELTS 1939 - 1956.

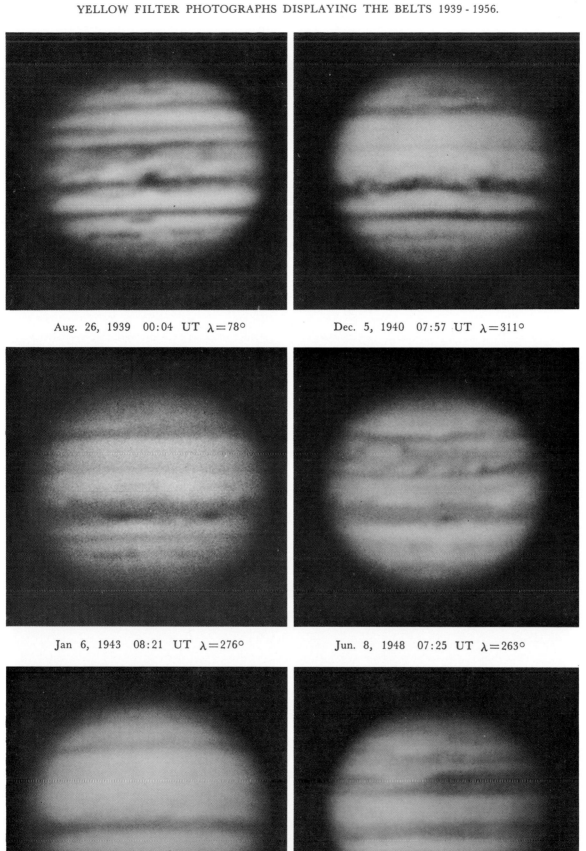

Aug. 26, 1939   00:04 UT $\lambda = 78°$ Dec. 5, 1940   07:57 UT $\lambda = 311°$

Jan 6, 1943   08:21 UT $\lambda = 276°$ Jun. 8, 1948   07:25 UT $\lambda = 263°$

Oct. 9, 1952   07:12 UT $\lambda = 179°$ Feb. 22, 1956   05:31 UT $\lambda = 323°$

Plate XLIII

Plate XLIII shows a drawing of Jupiter by the expert planetary observer Phillips, made on December 19, 1917, alongside a photograph by Slipher obtained at Flagstaff on the same night but approximately one whole rotation later, portraying the preceding end of the South Tropical Disturbance. In general, the agreement is excellent, but in certain particulars such as the fine structure in the belts, rich detail in the equator, and in the full tonal gradations over the disk, the photograph excels.

Since these two observations differ in time by almost a whole rotation period of the planet, the Phillips observation caught certain satellite phenomena which were absent when the photograph was made. Therefore, there are present in the drawing some markings which require an explanation before a complete comparison can be made. The two bright, circular spots near the left side of the drawing and the dark circular spot in the southern part of the Southern Equatorial Belt are due to: 1) Satellite III in transit, upper bright spot; 2) Satellite I in transit, lower bright spot; 3) shadow of I, dark spot. This shadow, incidentally, overlies the smaller fainter dark spot on the planet which is visible in the photograph, and another dark spot farther to the right was recorded by both observers.

PLATE XLIII

COMPARISON OF DRAWING WITH PHOTOGRAPH OF THE SAME FACE OF JUPITER.

Dec. 19, 1917 18:45 UT $\lambda = 0°$
T. E. R. Phillips

Dec. 20, 1917 04:00 UT $\lambda = 337°$
Lowell Photograph

Plate XLIV

Shown in Plate XLIV are four blue photographs of the same face of Jupiter, obtained in 1928, showing rapid changes in the surface markings especially south of (above) the equator. The dark oval spot on the upper left side of the disk is the Great Red Spot, which changed color completely between October 5 and December 1. The rapid change in the South Equatorial and the South Tropical Zones between September 14 and December 1, 1928, is illustrated by the transformation of the broad white zone on September 15 into a series of intense dark markings, some of which have invaded the equatorial region in the last picture. This transformation from the brilliant white zone shown in the upper photographs into huge dark clouds (which eventually formed a new dark South Equatorial Belt), was coincidental with the fading out of its color and the Red Spot itself (see its bay at left side of the December 1 photograph).

The two conspicuous round spots in the North Equatorial Belt, one white and the other dark and thus strikingly resembling a satellite and its shadow, are real markings on Jupiter. They were first photographed in early September and repeatedly recorded later as the white one gradually advanced on the dark one until on December 1, 1928, when contact was made. Thereafter they rotated together as a single spot, at least until the close of the season's observations. The persistence of such small definite spots often enduring for weeks or months without change of form or size, is, under the turbulent Jovian conditions quite surprising. Strangely, the spot nearer to the pole was rotating faster; usually the higher the latitude, the slower the rotation.

Many other examples of long-lasting sharp spots have been observed through the years (see Plate XLVII) which maintained the same form and configuration for weeks on end. This apparent affinity between these small definite spots is very puzzling. Their apparent banding together suggests a small magnetic field.

PLATE XLIV

PHOTOGRAPHS OF THE SAME FACE OF JUPITER IN BLUE LIGHT SHOWING RAPID CHANGES

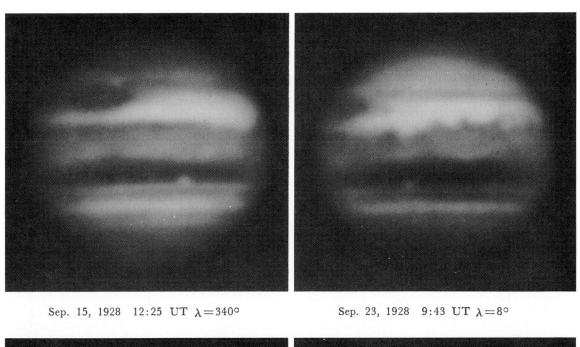

Sep. 15, 1928 12:25 UT $\lambda = 340°$ Sep. 23, 1928 9:43 UT $\lambda = 8°$

Oct. 5, 1928 9:15 UT $\lambda = 6°$ Dec. 1, 1928 01:23 UT $\lambda = 3°$

Plate XLV

Plate XLV shows photographs of Jupiter in yellow (left) and blue light (right) made at approximately the same time. Comparison of the two upper photographs demonstrates that the Red Spot (just below and to left of dark spot, which is a satellite shadow) was neutral in tint at that time (February 12, 1930). The belts appear with about the same contrast in the two photographs indicating that they also were virtually colorless.

Yellow (lower left) and blue (lower right) photographs taken on February 18, 1931[1], showed the Red Spot much darker in blue than in yellow images, revealing that the Red Spot had become duskier and redder than in 1930. The equatorial belts are also darker in the blue images showing that they too had changed to a redder hue. It is especially noteworthy that this group of photographs shows the belts and zones in a state of relative inactivity during a quiescent period when the planet would be termed 'normal' in appearance.

[1]Slipher, E. C., 1931, P.A.S.P., *43*, 241.

PLATE XLV

PHOTOGRAPHS SHOWING THE RED SPOT AS WHITE (UPPER) AND REDDISH (LOWER).

February 12, 1930

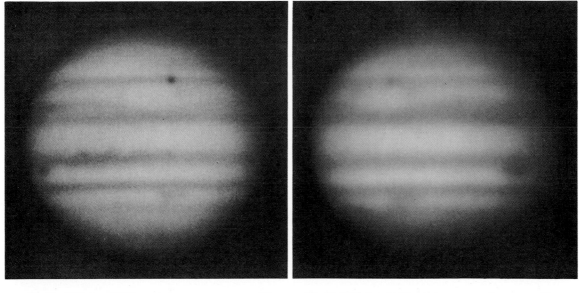

01:46 UT λ=277°   Y   02:43 UT λ=311°   B

February 18, 1931

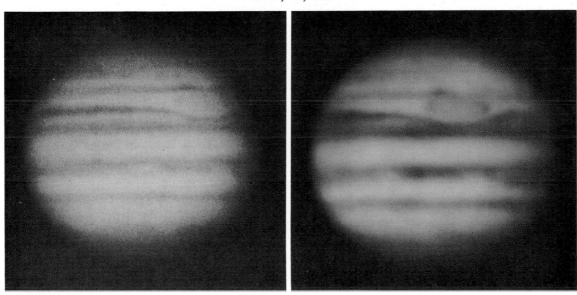

02:39 UT λ=226°   Y   03:10 UT λ=245°   B

Plate XLVI

Plate XLVI shows yellow photographs of Jupiter taken at Flagstaff from 1915 to 1940 which exhibit quiescent states of the planet in 1915 and 1940, as contrasted with states of great activity as denoted by the complex structure in the two 1938 pictures. Satellite I and its shadow are seen at right edge of the planet on August 11.

The bay of the Red Spot is near the right side of the first photograph and it is identified by its chrysalis near the center of image number two.

92

PLATE XLVI

PHOTOGRAPHS SHOWING THE BELTS OF JUPITER IN DISTURBED AND QUIESCENT STATES.

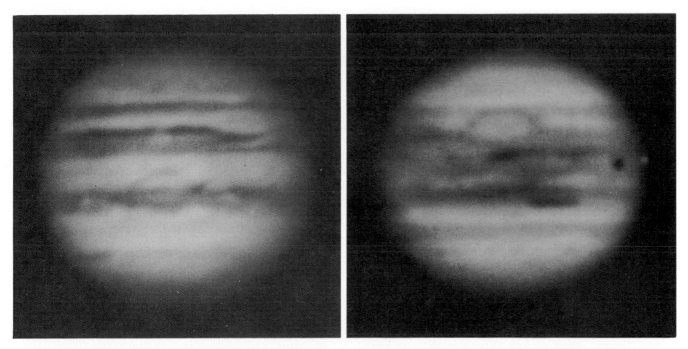

Oct. 20, 1915 02:29 UT λ＝138°   Aug. 11, 1938 07:02 UT λ＝148°

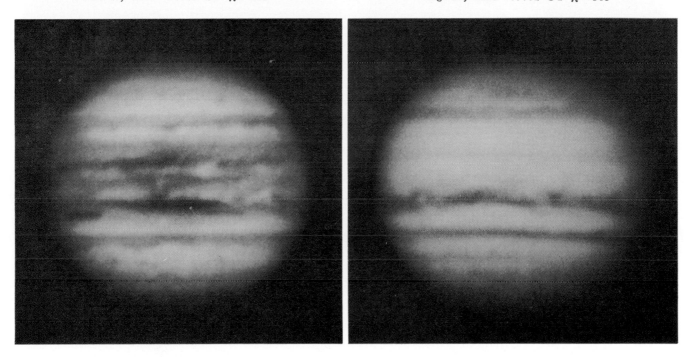

Aug. 9, 1938 07:19 UT λ＝217°   Dec. 5, 1940 07:57 UT λ＝311°

Plate XLVII

The two pairs of identical photographs, taken 49½ hours apart, and shown in Plate XLVII portray singular phenomena accompanying the conjunction of dark spots with the Red Spot which appears above the center of the disk. The dark spots, to the left of the Red Spot, drifted to the right and showed an unprecedentedly long rotation of 9^h59^m, while the spots below along the South Equatorial Zone advanced rapidly to the left in accord with a rotation of about 9^h51^m. These two very different regimes of rotation, combined with that of $9^h55^m.7$ for the Red Spot, produced such rapid shifting of the objects in the picture that changes were recognized after a lapse of an hour or so.

Two identical composite photographs for each date are shown here side by side for both the 5th and 7th, thereby providing the reader ready means for verifying the reality of every detail of the comparison.

As the row of dark spots, well shown in the photographs of Sep. 24, Plate XLVIII, retrograded past the Red Spot they were definitely deflected northwards and passed through a narrow channel between the Red Spot's northern border and the southern part of the South Equatorial Belt. In so doing they sometimes appeared to contact similar markings advancing oppositely past the Red Spot; the relative motion between these two sets of spots was approximately 8,000 miles per day. Somehow during this passage all the retrograding spots were destroyed, as none emerged in the bright zone following the Red Spot. During these conjunctions in October, new dark areas, however, began to appear in the bright zone following the Red Spot (see Plate XLIV); the appearance and growth of which may be related to the disappearance of the dark spots.

The successive conjunctions of this series of spots with the Red Spot were accompanied by numerous changes in the shape of the Red Spot and its deterioration in color and intensity. Changes in form resulted from obscuration, displacement, or deflection of the dark ring, which outlines the Spot, and from the merging of or adherence of dark spots. The dark shoulder extending above the curved outline near the south following end in the photographs of Oct. 5, is a distinct change from the elliptical form photographed on Oct. 4 and is not noticeable on Oct. 7. On October 11 a dark linear streak was seen extending entirely across the following part of the Spot in a northeast-southwest direction. Photographs of October 18 and 19 (not included) show southward displacement of its northern boundary by hundreds of miles giving the Spot a flat northern base. This, combined with dark extensions at the preceding and following ends, caused it to be temporarily longer and narrower than on other nights. Most of the phenomena described here lasted only a single night.

The intimate reactions between the various markings described above strongly indicate that they are all at approximately the same level, and in some instances higher than the Red Spot. If this conclusion is true it casts doubt on the validity of certain theories explaining the physical nature of the Red Spot[1] and militates strongly against others[2].

---

[1] Wildt, Rupert, 1939, Proc. Am. Phil. Soc., *81*, No. 2.
[2] Peek, B. M., 1939, Jr. of B.A.A., *50*, No. 1.

PLATE XLVII
RAPID RELATIVE MOTION OF SPOTS WITHIN INTERVAL OF FIFTY HOURS

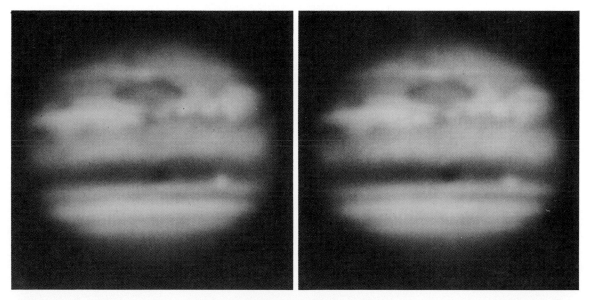

Oct. 5, 1928 08:10 UT $\lambda = 317°$

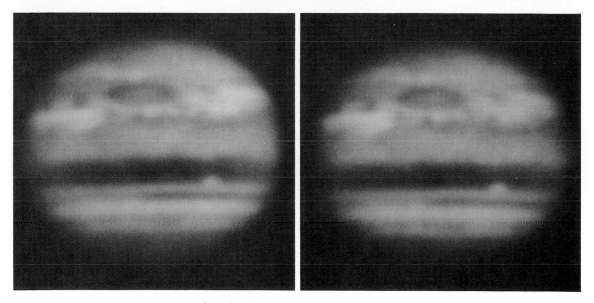

Oct. 7, 1928 09:58 UT $\lambda = 324°$

Plate XLVIII

The two yellow photographs of Jupiter in the top row were taken 69 hours apart on October 5 and 8, 1928, during a period of abnormal activity on the planet. The Red Spot is nearly one-half way from the center toward the left edge of the disk. Close inspection of these negatives, although taken less than seventy hours apart, reveals appreciable change in the markings. These two photographs disclose that the spots and wisps in the northern edge of the Equatorial Zone advanced toward the left with respect to markings in the North Equatorial Belt during the seventy hour interval.

Two views of Jupiter photographed in yellow light 14 days apart are shown below; they record the same group of great, leaning wisps across the equator and also display marked alterations in the intricate detail of the South Tropical Zone (above the equator). The spectacular strength of the wisps, so far as is known to the author, as great as ever witnessed, is probably related to the great activity in the turbulent region south of the equator. The wisps suggest strong cross-winds.

Attention is called to the row of dark spots in the latitude of the southern edge of the South Equatorial Belt, conspicuous in the September 24 photograph, because of the significant role they played as they retrograded past the Red Spot during October (see Plate XLVII).

96

PLATE XLVIII

RAPID CHANGES IN THE EQUATORIAL WISPS AND BELT STRUCTURE DURING A BRIEF INTERVAL.

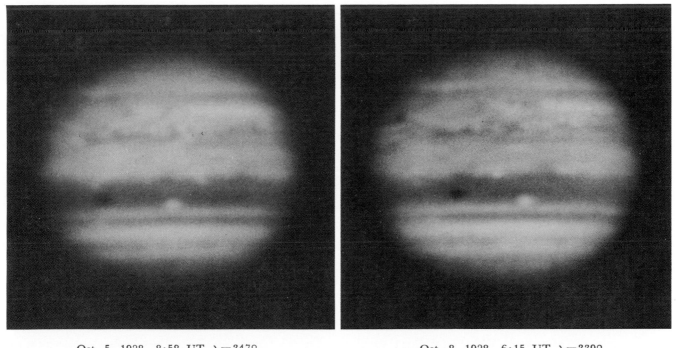

Oct. 5, 1928 8:58 UT $\lambda=347°$ Oct. 8, 1928 6:15 UT $\lambda=339°$

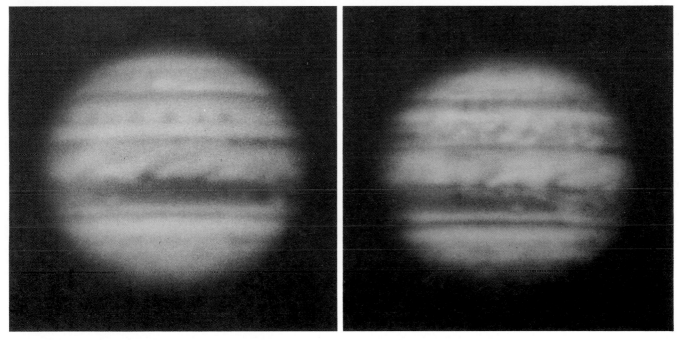

Sep. 24, 1928 11:01 UT $\lambda=179°$ Oct. 8, 1928 08:43 UT $\lambda=68°$

Plate XLIX

Plate XLIX shows (top row) red and blue photographs taken at approximately the same time on January 31, 1930. The South Equatorial Belt comes out broad and dark in the blue image, but in the red picture the belt is scarcely visible. Visually this belt appeared rosy-red. Selective reflection caused the belt to photograph bright in red light, the contrast thus being reduced[1] while in blue light it was weak and showed quite dark. Note that the Red Spot at the upper left side in both photographs showed white in both colors, thus demonstrating that it was colorless.

The three lower photographs illustrate motions across the central latitudes of Jupiter. The 1926 picture shows no evidence of cross currents and dark material crossing the Equatorial Zone, but the crisscross streaks and wisps crossing the mid-latitudes in 1927 and 1928 appear to mark the transport of dark material by north-south currents.

---

[1]Slipher, E. C., 1931, P.A.S.P., *43*, 254; p. 241, Plate X, Fig. 5.

PLATE XLIX

BLUE AND RED PHOTOGRAPHS DEMONSTRATING EXTREME REDNESS OF THE SOUTHERN EQUATORIAL BELT.

Jan. 31, 1930 03:32 UT λ= 339° R   Jan. 31, 1930 03:53 UT λ= 351° B

PHOTOGRAPHS INDICATING MOTION CROSS-WISE TO BELTS.

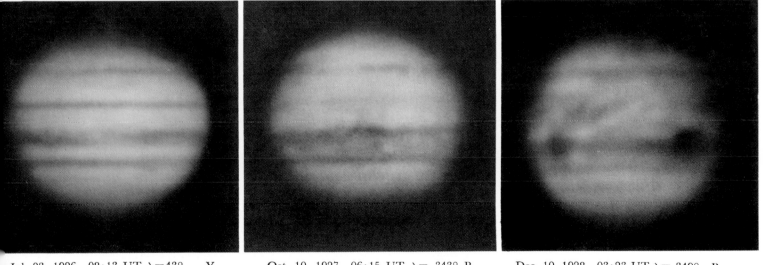

Jul. 23, 1926 08:13 UT λ=43°   Y   Oct. 10, 1927 06:15 UT λ= 343° R   Dec. 10, 1928 03:23 UT λ= 349° R

Plate L

In Plate L three sets of tri-color photographs (green, red, and blue) illustrate various degrees of coloration on Jupiter between 1937 and 1949. They show the intense redness of the Red Spot in 1937, the strong reddish color of the South Equatorial and Tropical Belts in 1938, as contrasted with the neutral tints shown by the remarkable lack of differences in green, red, and blue photographs of 1949. The red tints are demonstrated by the darkness of the Red Spot in blue light in 1937 as contrasted to its invisibility in the companion red image; and the rosy tint of the South Equatorial Belt in 1938 is likewise revealed by its darkness in blue light, (while the companion red image scarcely shows it at all) although certain bluish markings near the equator show dark and strong in the same image. These examples clearly demonstrate the effect of selective reflection and the power of the photograph in colorimetric studies. Such tri-color sets of photographs provide excellent copies in natural colors by the Kodak Dye Transfer Process.

PLATE L

COLOR PHOTOGRAPHS OF THE SAME FACE OF JUPITER REVEALING THE INTENSE REDNESS OF THE RED SPOT AND SOME BELTS.

Jun. 15, 1937

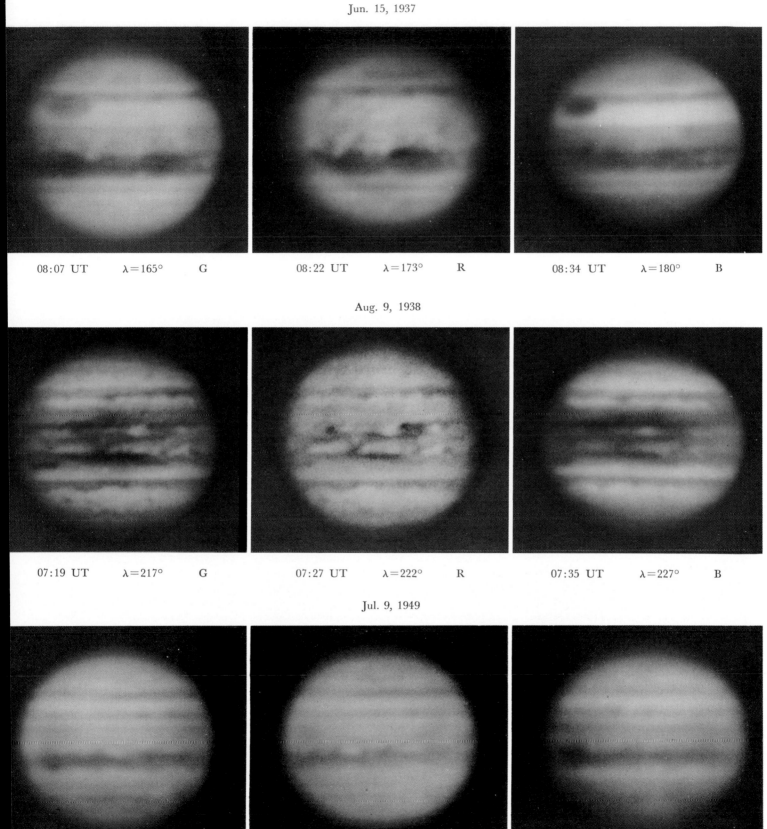

| 08:07 UT | λ=165° | G | 08:22 UT | λ=173° | R | 08:34 UT | λ=180° | B |

Aug. 9, 1938

| 07:19 UT | λ=217° | G | 07:27 UT | λ=222° | R | 07:35 UT | λ=227° | B |

Jul. 9, 1949

| 08:10 UT | λ=2° | G | 08:35 UT | λ=19° | R | 08:58 UT | λ=33° | B |

Plate LI

Plate LI shows two sets of tricolor (red, yellow, and blue) photographs of Jupiter taken on July 24, 1938. A group of markings in the equatorial region of the planet, noted visually as bluish, photographed distinctly darker in the red than in the yellow and blue light. This confirmed the visual estimate of color. Spots with strong bluish tints are rare on Jupiter. The slender dark marking in the North Equatorial Belt near the middle of the disk actually showed fainter in red than in yellow and blue images, denoting that its color was reddish. By similar analysis the color of various other markings in these images can be readliy determined.

The foregoing color-filter photographs indicate that the Sun's rays penetrate the gaseous atmosphere of Jupiter freely to the cloud level, and unlike the violet layer and clouds on Mars, the rays emerge again without any sensible screening or veiling effects. For this reason the obvious differences between the photographs taken in different colors arise from selective reflection: i.e. the red markings appearing white or bright in red photographs and very dark in blue light.

However, strong absorption bands in the red end of the Jovian spectrum, due to ammonia and methane in its atmosphere, produce noticeable limb darkening in photographs taken in deep red or infrared light.

PLATE LI

TRICOLOR PHOTOGRAPHS OF THE SAME FACE OF JUPITER REVEALING STRONG DIFFERENCES OF VARIOUS SPOTS.

July 24, 1938

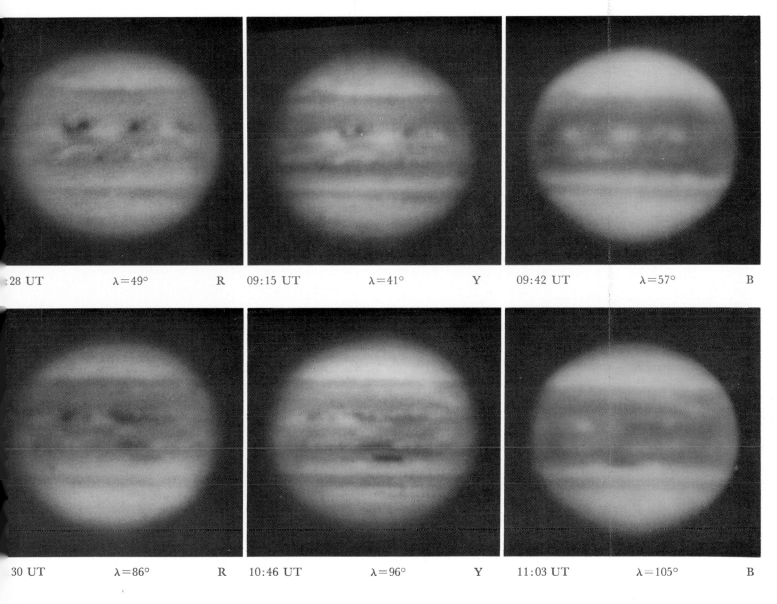

:28 UT $\lambda = 49°$ R   09:15 UT $\lambda = 41°$ Y   09:42 UT $\lambda = 57°$ B

30 UT $\lambda = 86°$ R   10:46 UT $\lambda = 96°$ Y   11:03 UT $\lambda = 105°$ B

Plate LII

These two blue photographs of Jupiter taken in 1928 display great turbulence over much of the southern hemisphere, as can be seen from the broken, disrupted appearance of the belts and vivid spots (quiescence is generally marked by smooth parallel belts and zones). The disturbance was particularly noticeable in the South Equatorial and Tropical Belts, as well as by the filling up of the equatorial bright zone with dark material, especially evident in the November 24 photograph. A peculiar gap can be seen in the South Equatorial Belt near the central meridian where dark material appears to be flowing northward across the equator.

PLATE LII

JUPITER — GREATLY DISTURBED CONDITION OF SOUTHERN HEMISPHERE.

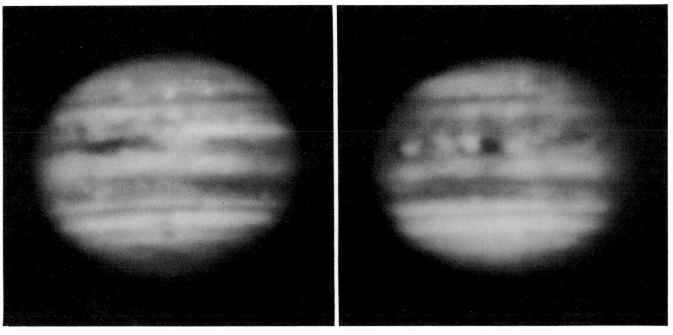

Oct. 20, 1928   10:04 UT   λ=122°   Nov. 24, 1928   06:26 UT   λ=214°

Plate LIII

It is well known that spots on Jupiter sometimes travel at different rates, even in the same latitude. In these photographs taken in 1936 we see the rare case of two small dark spots, that gradually approached each other until contact occurred, merging into a single spot. The two spots are visible on the North Equatorial Belt on the July 7 image (they had been observed for some time previously); on July 23 they became a single spot and a careful watch showed they did not separate again.

It was noted visually that, as conjunction of these spots occurred, the upper (southern) one appeared to flow into the lower one, as if drawn into a vortex.

106

PLATE LIII

JUPITER — THE MERGING OF TWO DARK SPOTS.

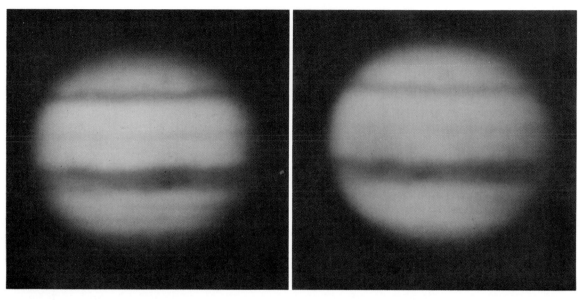

Jul 7, 1936   5:45 UT $\lambda = 84°$ Y   Jul. 23, 1936   05:23 UT $\lambda = 286°$ Y

Plate LIV

These yellow photographs of Saturn made in 1904 to 1909 display various tilts of the rings, changes in the shadow of the ball on the rings, and also exhibit marked changes in the belts on the ball. In the 1904 image the earth was 2°2 higher than the sun above the ring-plane, and in consequence of the phase effect and particle-shadowing, the rings appear much darker than the ball. In 1904 the planet shows a very wide, bright zone at the equator, a wide, dark belt in the tropics and a brighter zone toward the north pole. In the 1909 picture, the ball is dusky with the two ill-defined, diffuse belts, and it also shows the shadow of the rings on the ball along the lower edge of the rings. In 1911 and 1912, a series of belts are shown, and the ball shines through Cassini's Division and Ring A where the rings cross the ball.

PLATE LIV

VARIOUS ASPECTS OF SATURN 1904 - 1912.

Nov. 29, 1904

Nov. 4, 1909

Oct. 11, 1911

Dec. 23, 1912

Plate LV

In Plate LV four yellow photographs of Saturn taken in 1913, 1915, 1916, and 1917, show different tilts of the ring system, shadows of the ball on the rings, strong belts, and dark caps over the south pole (top) which are especially distinct in 1916. Again the ball can readily be seen through Cassini's Division and the exterior ring. The photographs reveal appreciable change in position and strength of the belts on the ball. In 1917 the dark tropical belt shows sharp and very intense, and the original negative shows a faint gray line running centrally through the equatorial zone.

PLATE LV
VARIOUS ASPECTS OF SATURN 1913 - 1917.

Jan. 17, 1913

Mar. 12, 1915

Feb. 11, 1916

Feb. 8, 1917

Plate LVI

The examples of yellow photographs in Plate LVI show Saturn in 1920 when the earth was south of the ring plane; and in 1921 when the earth was exactly in the plane of the rings; after that date we view the north side of the rings. In these pictures we observe a very dark sash across the middle of the ball in 1921 produced by the edge-on rings and their shadow cast upon the ball; and in 1922 the shadow of the rings on the ball shows along their upper edge. In 1920 as in 1909 (see Plate LIV) the ball appears nearly uniform and beltless, a condition which always seems to occur with a low inclination of the planet's equator. The belt pattern on the ball distinctly differs on each of these six negatives.

On June 18, 1921, when the Earth and Sun as seen from Saturn differed in declination by about 2°50′ the writer saw the rings and their shadow projected on the ball as two separate lines. This phenomenon had not been seen before.

112

PLATE LVI

VARIOUS ASPECTS OF SATURN 1920 - 1929

Mar. 19, 1920   Apr. 22, 1921

May 24, 1922   Jul. 8, 1926

May 24, 1927   Sep. 14, 1929

Plate LVII

The six examples of yellow photographs of Saturn in Plate LVII were obtained from 1933 to 1940. They display various aspects of the ball and the ring system seen from the north side of the ring plane (1933-1934) and the south (1937-1940). There is an obvious change in the markings on the ball between 1933 and 1934; especially noteworthy are the single dark belt and the large whitish cap over the southern polar regions in 1934. In 1940 the equatorial bright zone is much narrower and brighter than normal. In 1936, as the photograph shows, the plane of the rings passed through the earth as in 1921.

114

PLATE LVII
VARIOUS ASPECTS OF SATURN 1933 - 1940.

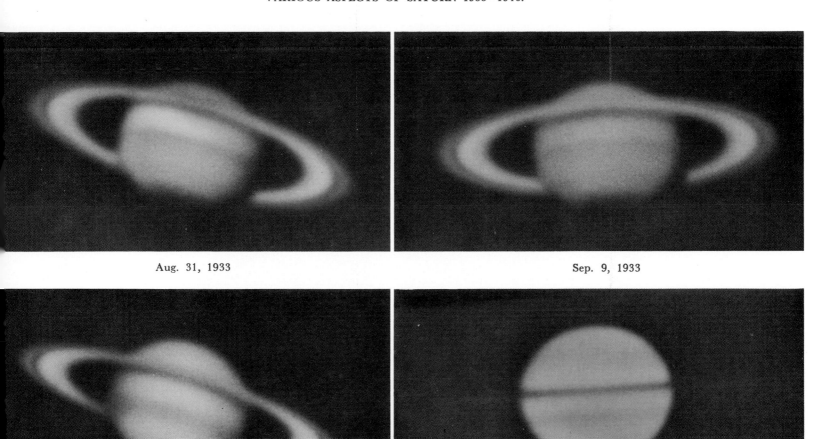

Aug. 31, 1933   Sep. 9, 1933

Sep. 18, 1934   Jul. 29, 1936

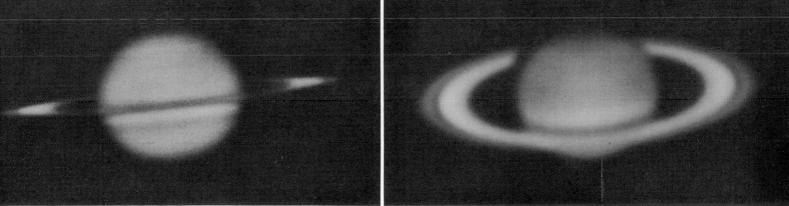

Oct. 1, 1937   Oct. 17, 1940

Plate LVIII

The four yellow photographs of Saturn in Plate LVIII display a remarkable series of fine belts on the ball, some reaching nearly to the pole, especially in 1941. In 1943 and 1945 the dark polar cap is enhanced. A change in the broad, dark equatorial belt is evident between 1941 and 1946, marked by the dark core which appeared there in 1945 and 1946. The Crepe Ring is easily seen where it crosses the ball. In these photographs the ball unmistakably shines through Cassini's Division and the outer ring in all of the images, which denotes the great sparsity of particles present in these areas.

116

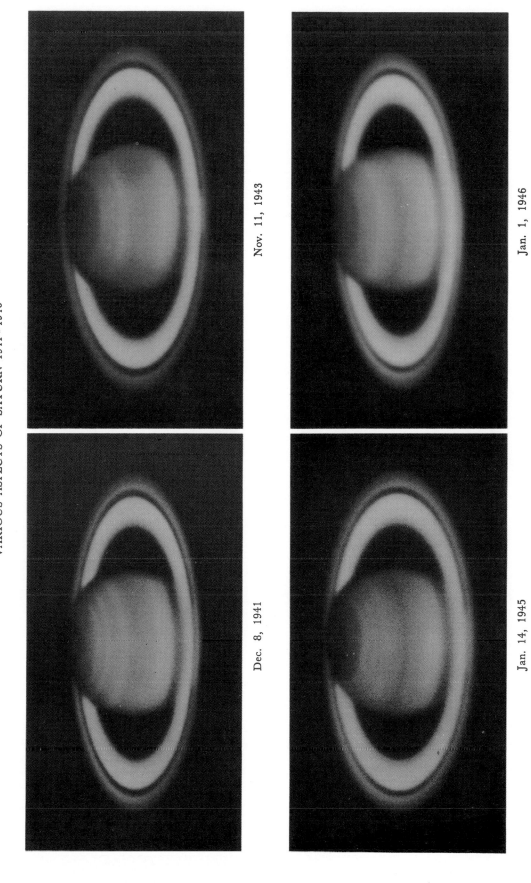

PLATE LVIII

VARIOUS ASPECTS OF SATURN 1941 - 1946

Nov. 11, 1943

Jan. 1, 1946

Dec. 8, 1941

Jan. 14, 1945

Plate LIX

The two photographs in Plate LIX show the planet from opposite sides of the ring plane. In 1948 the ball shows distinct belts and a large dark polar cap and the rings are darkly outlined across the ball by their own shadow and the Crepe Ring. In 1952 these markings are gone and the ball is featureless except for the bright equatorial zone. The dull, featureless condition of the ball in 1952, with low inclination of the equator, is an almost exact repetition of its appearance in like circumstances in 1909 and 1920. (See Plates LIV and LVI.)

While considerable changes occur on the surface of Saturn they are far less conspicuous than those noted on Jupiter, the general absence of striking features is much greater than can be accounted for by Saturn's greater distance. The changes in the belts of Saturn shown by these photographs not only occur more slowly, are less spectacular, and never seem to develop to the depth of intensity displayed by the dark markings on Jupiter. Also, as the tri-color photographs show (Plate LI), marked and widespread color changes occur; but none of these examples display anything like the brilliant colors so often portrayed by Jupiter. To account for this characteristic difference no satisfactory explanation has been advanced, beyond the obvious effect of the lower surface temperature on Saturn.

PLATE LIX

VARIOUS ASPECTS OF SATURN IN 1948 AND 1952.

Mar. 22, 1948   Y

Apr. 18, 1952   Y

Plate LX

In Plate LX the extreme faintness of the rings on July 16, 1937, was caused by the earth being higher above the ring plane than was the sun, so that each particle of the rings shadowed the next behind it. This produced a phase-effect causing a dusky appearance of the rings which appeared unusually dark compared to the ball. On October 1, 1937, the reverse situation existed, the sun then being higher above the rings than the earth; all the visible surface of the rings was fully illuminated and the rings again showed their full brightness. Similar fluctuations in the brightness of the rings have been photographed on a number of occasions and indicate that the particles of the rings consist of opaque material[1].

The photograph taken on July 29, 1936, shows the planet when the earth was nearly in the plane of the ring system, in which aspect the rings compared to the ball always become quite faint but never entirely invisible in a moderately large refractor.

[1]Slipher, E. C., 1938b, Proc. Am .Phil. Soc., *79*, 3, p. 464, Plate VIII, Figs. 5 and 6.

PLATE LX

SATURN—ILLUMINATION EFFECTS WHEN THE RINGS ARE NEARLY EDGEWISE.

Jul. 16, 1937   Oct. 1, 1937

Jul. 29, 1936

Plate LXI

In Plate LXI are two sets of tri-color photographs of Saturn (1940 and 1943) which clearly display the effect of color on the ball. Tri-color negatives over a period of thirty years have indicated that the rings shine essentially by white light, which is consonant with spectrographic results. Using the neutral rings as a basis of comparison, it is obvious that all of the ball except the equatorial bright zone appears markedly darker in blue than in either red or yellow; especially is this true of the South Tropical region, which denotes that these particular portions of the ball are distinctly redder than the rings. Sometimes the equatorial zone is strongly tinted too, as for example in 1927, when it photographed as a conspicuously dark sash in blue and ultraviolet light, as it was recorded by Wood (1916)[1] and Wright (1927)[2]. Usually, but not invariably, the tropical regions of Saturn show a faint reddish tint.

In the blue image in 1943 the south polar cap shows relatively darker than in yellow and red, suggesting that it must have been somewhat reddish in color.

Spectra of the ball and rings from $\lambda 3500$ to $\lambda 7600$ taken alongside each other, on the same plate for comparison, indicate that the reflected light is essentially the same except for absorption by methane and a trace of ammonia. Therefore, they give no evidence that the rings consist of snow or ice as suggested by some.

---

[1]Wood, R. W., 1916, Ap.J., *43,* p. 314.
[2]Wright, W. H., 1927, P.A.S.P., *39,* p. 231, Plate 28.

PLATE LXI

TRICOLOR OBSERVATIONS OF SATURN IN 1940 AND 1943.

Oct. 17, 1940

Nov. 12, 1943

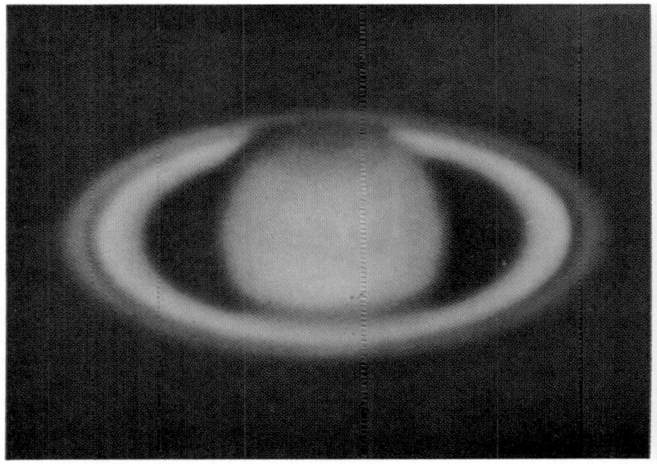

B

Y

R

B

Y

R

Plate LXII

Plate LXII shows yellow photographs covering the remarkable outburst of white spots which appeared successively in Saturn's equatorial zone at intervals between August 3 and October 1, 1933. The appearance of these spots permitted a new determination of Saturn's equatorial rotation period almost for the first time since the famous Hall Spot in 1876[1].

The photographs of August 9 and August 27 show Spot I with about equal brightness but slightly longer on August 27; on August 18 it had extended over nearly one-half the planet's diameter.

The photograph of August 28 (second row, left) shows an entirely new Spot II on the night of its discovery at the Lowell Observatory. Spot II, as the photograph shows, was quite as bright as the first, but smaller and more sharply defined, appearing here as a notch in the Crepe Ring 75° behind Spot I in longitude.

On August 31, Spot I appears much the same as before, though slightly longer. On September 6, (third row, left) Spot II, and on September 11, Spot I, exhibit an enormous expansion in the direction of the planet's rotation until Spot I extended two-thirds the way across the disk, meanwhile maintaining the same width and brightness. In the growth and the direction of expansion of these two spots, they repeated exactly the behavior of the Hall Spot of 1876. Soon after this great expansion of the first two spots it was discovered that they were the forerunners of a whole series of small, individual spots scattered all the way around the equator. Before the end of September, nineteen spots had been photographed and had their longitudes determined by assuming Spot I as the zero meridian.

By timing the transits of the main spot and one other during 211 revolutions of the planet a rotation period of $10^h14^m24^s2$ was derived for Saturn. This agrees closely with the period of $10^h14^m23^s8$ obtained by Asaph Hall from a similar great white spot in December, 1876.

From spectrographic and temperature results it seems probable that these white spots were due to ammonia vapor emerging from the interior of the ball and freezing as it reached the surface.

---

[1]Hall, A., 1885, Washington Observations, Appendix II.

PLATE LXII

SATURN — DEVELOPMENT OF THE WHITE SPOTS IN 1933.

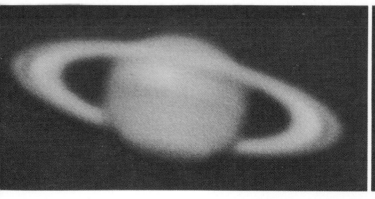

Aug. 9, 1933   Spot I $\lambda = 26°$

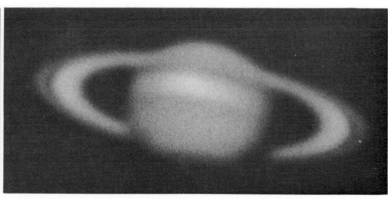

Aug. 27, 1933   Spot I $\lambda = 22°$

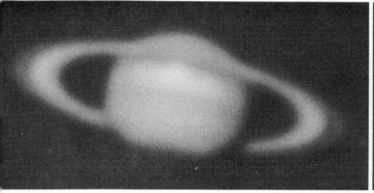

Aug. 28, 1933   Spot II $\lambda = 83°$

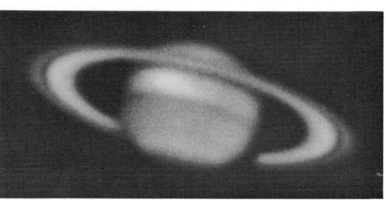

Aug. 31, 1933   Spot I $\lambda = 30°$

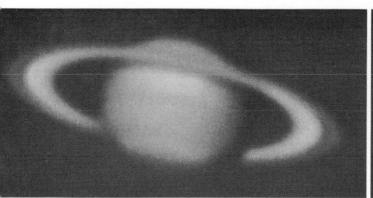

Sep. 6, 1933   Spot II $\lambda = 77°$

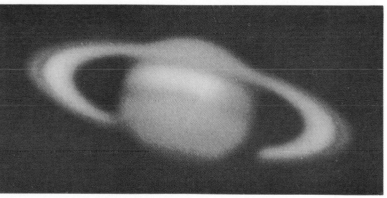

Sep. 11, 1933   Spot I $\lambda = 10°$

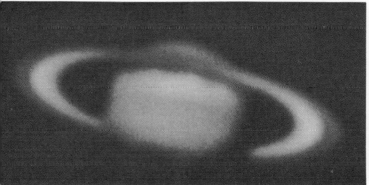

Sep. 21, 1933   New Spot $\lambda = 159°$

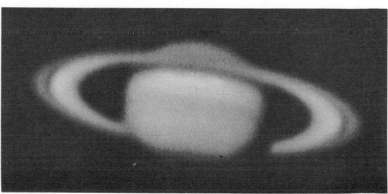

Sep. 26, 1933   New Spot $\lambda = 0°$